Leeds' Sculpture Collections Illustrated Concise Catalogue

Compiled by
Matthew Withey

Co-ordinated by
Jackie Howson
with the assistance of
Sophie Raikes

Henry Moore Institute
2006

Published in 2006 by
The Henry Moore Institute
74 The Headrow
Leeds
LS1 3AH

ISBN 1 905462 03 4

Compiled by
Matthew Withey

Coordinated by
Jackie Howson
and Sophie Raikes

Edited by
Penelope Curtis

Design + production
Groundwork, Skipton

Printed in England by
Wyke Printers, Hull

Photo credits: A majority of the
photographs has been commissioned
from Jerry Hardman-Jones and
Richard Littlewood, the remainder
comes from the acquisition files
and can be credited to Larkfield
Photography

Cover: Frederico Câmara,
Sleep (Leeds City Art Gallery, 2006)
photographic print

The Henry Moore Institute is part
of the Henry Moore Foundation
www.henry-moore-fdn.co.uk

Contents

Preface

It is ten years since we last published a concise catalogue of the sculpture collections which are owned by Leeds Museums & Galleries and curated by the Henry Moore Institute. In this time the collections have developed considerably, not least because in 1999 we were able to merge the Henry Moore Centre for the Study of Sculpture into the Henry Moore Institute, and to integrate the Institute's various activities relating to collections, exhibitions and research.[1]

In the intervening period we have published a guide to the archive entitled *The Sculpture Business* (1997), a catalogue of works on paper by sculptors (1999), a supplement to the first concise catalogue (2001), a two-volume companion guide to *Sculpture in 20th-century Britain* (2003) (with the second volume devoted to essays on the 175 sculptors in our collections born after 1850) and Victoria Worsley's concise inventory of our Archive holdings (2005).

As my short preface to the second volume of *Sculpture in 20th-century Britain,* and my longer introduction to the *Archive Guide* explain, our aim in this period has been to amplify the conventional narrative of modern British sculpture, to respond to opportunities to save individual sculptors' records, and to use the sculpture collection as a way of highlighting that broader-based history which often exists outside of the gallery itself.

At the same time we have also responded to particular opportunities to purchase valuable singular sculptures, and, on occasion, to introduce the work of younger exponents into this more historical collection. Notable examples acquired since 1996 include important works by Alexander Calder, Phillip King, Helen Chadwick and William Turnbull; important contemporary pieces by Eva Rothschild, Alison Wilding and Keith Wilson, as well as works which might be termed as 'curiosities' by neglected sculptors such as Barry Hart, Bruce Lacey and Marlow Moss, or surprising pieces such as Richard Long's 'Untitled (Pot)'.

This work has been made possible by the commitment of the small team at the Henry Moore Institute: colleagues who have followed up leads, visited collections in far-flung corners, and kept in touch with their owners as negotiations proceeded. Jon Wood and Victoria Worsley have been very active in working with artists and their families, as was Matthew Withey, who has now been succeeded by Sophie Raikes. All of us have been supported by Jackie Howson, a nearly constant presence in the recent history of our collection-building, and by Gill Armstrong.

We all share a belief in the importance of the collection as a living response to past activity. Our team, though small, is successful in attracting donations, as well as funding, to support our activities, not least, I suspect, because artists' families, and artists themselves, see the Institute as an organism which functions more organically than bureaucratically, and which can make things happen with their legacies. Our collections have grown, in large part, because people believe in us, and so, I hope, we shall be able to repay their trust, either in the short term, by publishing these acquisitions and encouraging research into them, or, in the longer term, by showing them to advantage in a re-furbished City Art Gallery. Certain gifts – which include works by Kenneth Armitage, Anthony Caro, Hubert Dalwood, Garth Evans, Alfred Hardiman, Gertrude Hermes, Eric Kennington, Martin Naylor, Peter Peri and Albert Toft – are more or less explicit tributes to what we are trying to achieve.

For the meantime, this new catalogue acts as an invitation to all to find out more about what we have inherited from our predecessors, and what we have brought into the collections in more recent years. It is a small tribute to those who have placed their trust in us, whether they be artists, heirs or the organisations which make it possible for institutions such as Leeds Museums & Galleries to continue to enrich their collections.[2]

Penelope Curtis
Curator
Henry Moore Institute

1   Approximately 200 sculptures have been added to the catalogue in this period; 24 of these (largely busts) have long been in the Leeds' collections, but were not in the sculpture catalogue because they were housed in other civic buildings. A further 6 works have been transferred from other Leeds collections. 21 maquettes by W H Thornycroft were transferred from Reading University as a result of the efforts of Martina Droth. Of this number, 68 were gifts and the Kenneth Armitage bequest numbered 13 maquettes.

2   At the time of writing the annual acquisitions grant for all Leeds Museums & Galleries (7 different institutions) is £35,000. The sculpture collection is also developed by this means, and is largely housed in the City Art Gallery, with pre-20th century pieces generally going on show in either Temple Newsam House or Lotherton Hall. The archive, held at the Henry Moore Institute, and the collections of works on paper by sculptors, are developed by means of a budget allocated by the Henry Moore Foundation, but title is made over to the city. The external bodies which make it possible for us to expand our collections – the MLA/V&A Purchase Grant Fund, the NACF, the LACF, the CAS and the HLF – are credited individually wherever appropriate, and listed in full at the beginning. 16 works were acquired with grant aid from one or more of these organisations.

Catalogue details

This catalogue includes acquisitions up to December 2005.
Works are ordered by artist's name, and then by date of production.

The entries are given in the following order:

Artist (with dates)
Accession number
Title and date of work *
Medium
Height × depth × width in centimetres
Details of acquisition

* Where educated guesses have been made concerning dates of
production, these are indicated by c for circa

Where the letters A and D are appended to the entry, they indicate
the existence of supplementary holdings in our collections:

A   =   Archive

D   =   Drawings

List of Abbreviations

CAS   Contemporary Art Society

HLF   Heritage Lottery Fund

HMF   Henry Moore Foundation

HMI   Henry Moore Institute

LACF   Leeds Art Collections Fund

MLA   Museums, Libraries and Archives Council

NACF   National Art Collections Fund

NHMF   National Heritage Memorial Fund

T   Temporary (after an accession number)

V&A   Victoria & Albert Museum

Please note that Government grants awarded for purchases before
1 April 2000 are referred to as V&A Purchase Grant Fund grants and
after 1 April 2000 referred to as MLA/V&A Purchase Grant Fund.

Purchases without credits were bought wholly with funds provided
by the City of Leeds

Robert Adams 1917–1984

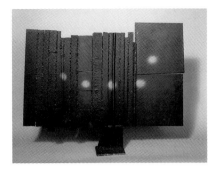

1997.0045
Rising Movement I, 1962
Bronze
56 × 71 × 10cm
Purchased with the aid of a grant from
the V&A Purchase Grant Fund, 1997

John Adams Acton 1830–1910

2005.0492
**Bust of William Ewart Gott (1827–
1879),** 1865
Marble
68 × 46 × 34cm
Transferred from Leeds City Museum,
1971

1904.0095
**Bust of Cardinal Henry Edward
Manning (1808–1892),** c.1884
Marble
87 × 72 × 41cm
Presented by Sir James Kitson, Lord
Airedale, 1904

2005.0507
**Bust of John Barran, Lord Airedale
(1821–1905),** c.1886
Marble
62 × 51 × 30cm
Acquisition source unknown

Thomas Allen c.1915–c.1987

1932.0025
The Bull, 1931
Portland stone
33.5 × 50 × 24cm
Purchased 1932

Edward Allington b.1951   A D

1995.0004
Fruit of Oblivion, 1982
Plastic grapes, unglazed ceramics, steel
and metal
127 × 64 × 72cm
Purchased from the artist with the aid
of grants from the V&A Purchase Grant
Fund and the LACF, 1995

1993.0010
**Garden Sculpture with Predetermined
Details,** 1989–90
MDF, cast concrete, gesso and carpet
felt
80 × 174 × 105cm
Purchased from the artist with the aid
of grants from the NACF and the HMF,
1993

Libero Andreotti 1875–1933

1950.0034
Bust of Donna Maria Chiapelli, c.1932
Bronze
54 × 26 × 26cm
Purchased with the aid of a grant from
the Corporation Fund, 1950

Anonymous Sculptors

1945.0018.0002
Head of a Man, 16th century
Painted wood
35 × 20 × 25cm
Presented by R.H. Kitson, 1945

1933.0025.0001
Bust of Septimus Severus (146–211 AD), 17th century
Marbles
76 × 49 × 21cm
Presented by Mrs Dorothy Una McGrigor-Phillips, 1933

1933.0025.0002
Bust of Caligula (12–41 AD), 17th century
Marbles
82 × 50 × 20cm
Presented by Mrs Dorothy Una McGrigor-Phillips, 1933

1933.0025.0003
Bust of Claudius (10 BC–54 AD), 17th century
Marbles
75 × 49 × 21cm
Presented by Mrs Dorothy Una McGrigor-Phillips, 1933

1933.0025.0004
Bust of Marcus Brutus (85–42 BC), 17th century
Marbles
77 × 51 × 18cm
Presented by Mrs Dorothy Una McGrigor-Phillips, 1933

1933.0025.0005
Bust of Nero (37–68 AD), 17th century
Marbles
77 × 50 × 20cm
Presented by Mrs Dorothy Una McGrigor-Phillips, 1933

1933.0025.0006
Bust of Lucius Verius (130–169 AD), 17th century
Marbles
77 × 49 × 20cm
Presented by Mrs Dorothy Una McGrigor-Phillips, 1933

1933.0025.0007
Bust of Vitellius (15–69 AD), 17th century
Marbles
70 × 49 × 25cm
Presented by Mrs Dorothy Una McGrigor-Phillips, 1933

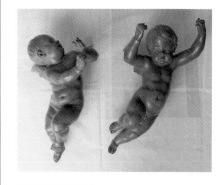

1952.0005.0515
Pair of Putti, early 18th century
Pine
43 × 27 × 21.5cm (approx)
Bequeathed by Agnes and Norman Lupton, 1952

1899.0001.T
Bust of Benjamin Disraeli (1804–1881), *c.*1840
Marble
70 × 57 × 31cm
Presented by Colonel T. Walter Harding, Lord Mayor of Leeds, 1899

1969.0199.0084 [E/1969/199/84]
Bust of a Woman with braided hair, 19th century
Plaster
34.5 × 24 × 17cm
Purchased 1969

1980.0034
Maquette for a Seated Man in Classical Dress, 19th century
Painted plaster
34 × 21 × 17cm
Presented by Cyril Humphris, 1980

1966.0089 [E/1969/89]
Bust of Christina Rossetti (1830–1894), late 19th century
Plaster
40.6 × 37 × 21cm
Purchased 1966

1950.0024
Bust of Mrs Beckett, *c.*1900
Marble
57 × 54 × 37cm
Presented by Mrs B. Egerton, 1950

2001.0013.T [E/ZO/6633]
Bust of James Keir Hardie (1856–1915), 1906
Painted plaster
40 × 19 × 13.5cm
Acquisition source unknown

Kenneth Armitage
1916–2002   D

2005.0046
Maquette for Linked Figures, 1948–9
Pink plaster
28.5 × 15.5 × 10cm
Bequeathed by the artist, 2004

2005.0049
Standing Figure, 1949
Wrought iron
24 × 10 × 6.5cm
Bequeathed by the artist, 2004

2005.0045
Maquette for Two Standing Figures, 1951
Pink plaster
35.5 × 23 × 6cm
Bequeathed by the artist, 2004

2005.0050
Standing Group, 1951
Pink plaster
26.5 × 26 × 8cm
Bequeathed by the artist, 2004

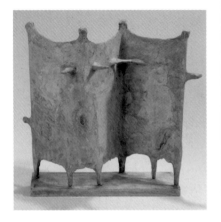

2005.0043
Maquette for Four Standing Figures,
1952
Pink plaster
28.5 × 26.5 × 11cm
Bequeathed by the artist, 2004

2005.0048
Flat Standing Figure, 1952
Bronze
31 × 12 × 6cm
Bequeathed by the artist, 2004

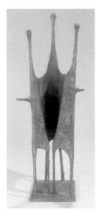

2005.0047
**Maquette for Standing Group 2
(Version E),** 1952
Pink plaster
39 × 13.5 × 12.5cm
Bequeathed by the artist, 2004

2005.0040
Maquette for Standing Group Two,
1952
Pink plaster
33.1 × 13 × 11cm
Bequeathed by the artist, 2004

2005.0041
Two Standing Figures, 1953
Pink plaster
75 × 56 × 14cm
Bequeathed by the artist, 2004

2005.0051
Children Playing, 1953
Bronze
26.5 × 31 × 9cm
Bequeathed by the artist, 2004

2005.0038
Maquette for Footballers, 1953
Coloured resin
51 × 25 × 21cm
Bequeathed by the artist, 2004

2005.0044
Roly Poly, 1955
Bronze
32.5 × 27.5 × 11.5cm
Bequeathed by the artist, 2004

2005.0042
Girl Without a Face, 1958–9
Bronze
37 × 10 × 9cm
Bequeathed by the artist, 2004

1965.0018.0001
Tower, 1963
Bronze
91 × 39 × 19cm
Purchased by the LACF, 1965

1985.0028.0002
Wall, 1965
Pewter
20 × 20 × 8cm
Presented by the beneficiaries of the
will of Christopher Hewitt (Mrs Beryl
Bjelke and Mrs Stella Saludes), 1985

1985.0028.0001
Single Figure with Drawing, 1972
Enamelled metal, charcoal and paper
54.5 × 25 × 25cm
Presented by the beneficiaries of the
will of Christopher Hewitt (Mrs Beryl
Bjelke and Mrs Stella Saludes), 1985

Henry Hugh Armstead
1828–1905   A D

1972.0037.0001
**Bust of John Deakin Heaton (1817–
1880),** 1882
Marble
80 × 66 × 33cm
Presented by United Leeds
Hospitals, 1972

Jean Arp 1885–1966   A

1965.0012

Threshold (Seuil Profil), 1960
Bronze
42 × 32 × 8.5cm
Purchased with the aid of a grant from the
Calouste Gulbenkian Foundation, 1965

Terry Atkinson b.1939   D

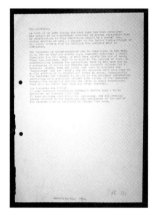

Awaiting accession no
Two Lectures. Schemas 1 to 6, 1968
(reconstructed 1994)
Typescript on paper
6 sheets at 29.7 × 21cm each
Purchased from the artist through the
HMI Archive Fund, 2003

Eric Bainbridge b.1955

2000.0050
Sugar, 1989
Plywood and white nylon fake fur
212.8 × 206.5 × 164.7cm
Presented by the artist, 2000

1995.0022
Eight Bronzes, 1993
Bronze
155 × 335 × 15cm (eight parts)
Purchased with the aid of grants from
the HMF and the Kenneth Hargreaves
Trust, 1995

Edward Bainbridge Copnall
1903–1973   A

2003.0026
Maquette for The Word of God, 1950
Plaster
59.5 × 14 × 11cm
Purchased through the HMI Archive
Fund, 2003

Thomas Banks   1735–1805   D

1968.0660.0007
Alcyone Discovering the Body of Ceyx,
1775–9
Marble
77.5 × 112cm
Presented as part of the Gascoigne
Bequest, 1968

Gilbert Bayes   1872–1953   A D

1982.0045.0002
**Medal Commemorating the Launch of
the Queen Mary,** 1936
Bronze
Diam. 7cm
Presented by Jacob Simon, 1982

Michel Léonard Béguine   1855–1929

1897.0088
La Charmeuse [The Snake Charmer],
1887
Bronze
40.7 × 15 × 20cm
Purchased 1897

William Behnes   1794–1864   D

1972.0002.T
Bust of Michael Sadler (1780–1835),
1836
Marble
73.7 × 46 × 36cm
Presented by United Leeds
Hospitals, 1972

2000.0059.T
Bust of Michael Sadler (1780–1835),
1836
Plaster
77 × 55 × 30cm
Acquisition source unknown

1972.0037.0002
Bust of William Hey (1796–1875), 1836
Plaster
84 × 54 × 27cm
Presented by United Leeds
Hospitals, 1972

Franta Belsky   1921–2000   A

2001.0084
The Lesson, 1955
Painted plaster
76 × 32 × 32cm
Purchased through the HMI Archive
Fund, 2001

Kuhne Beveridge 1877–?
and **Ella von Wrede** 1860–?

1901.0094
The Veiled Venus, 1900
Bronze
35 × 162.5 × 59cm
Presented anonymously, 1901

Peter Blake b.1932

1978.0021
Girl in a Window, 1962
Mixed media
123.7 × 112.3 × 33.5cm
Purchased with the aid of a grant from
the V&A Purchase Grant Fund, 1978

Phyllis M. Blundell *fl.*1924–1964

1972.0037.0003
Bust of a Man, 1924
Marble
68.6 × 59 × 37cm

Presented by the United Leeds
Hospitals, 1972

Neville Boden 1929–1996   A

1966.0021.0001
Procession Through a Split Curve, 1965
Polyurethane–painted mild steel
184 × 87.3 × 36cm
Purchased from the artist by the LACF,
1966

1966.0022.0001
The Titterary Tea Rose, 1965
Polyurethane-painted mild steel
183.6 × 75 × 31.5cm
Presented by Stanley Burton to the
LACF, 1966

1999.0022
Maquette, *c.*1965
Painted steel

20 × 6 × 5cm
Presented by Terry Friedman, 1999

1968.0030.0001
Relief No.6, 1967
Painted steel
91.5 × 68.5 × 17.5cm
Purchased by the LACF, 1968

Joseph Edward Boehm 1834–1890

1999.0047.0001
**Roundel Portrait of Francis William
Green,** 1872 (inset into mantelpiece)
Marble
Diam. 38cm
Purchased 1999

1999.0047.0002
**Roundel Portrait of Edward Lycett
Green (1860–1940),** 1872 (inset into
mantelpiece)
Marble
Diam. 38cm
Purchased 1999

Boyle Family

2005.0052
Chalk Cliff Study, 1999
Mixed media, resin and fiberglass
122 × 122 × 31.7cm
Purchased with the aid of grants from
the NACF and the MLA/V&A Purchase
Grant Fund, 2005

Laurence Bradshaw
1899–1978   A D

1995.0025
**Maquette for the Bronze Head of
Karl Marx (1818–1883) on the Marx
Memorial in Highgate Cemetery,
London,** 1954–5
Resin and bronze powder
17 × 21.5 × 12cm
Presented by Mrs Eileen Bradshaw,
1995

Ian Breakwell 1943–2005
and **Mike Leggett** b.1945   A

2005.0455.1
UNWORD, 1970 (digitally reconstructed 2003)
DVD projection, black and white,
16mm
Purchased with the aid of a grant from
the MLA/V&A Purchase Grant Fund
and the Henry Moore Institute Archive
Fund, 2005

Stuart Brisley b.1933

2005.0061
Twenty Six Hours Vienna, 1976
Twenty-six framed photographs
43 × 55 × 2.6cm (each)
Purchased through the HMI Archive
Fund, 2004

2005.0060
Easy Chair, 1986
Framed photograph
45 × 58 × 2.5cm
Purchased through the HMI Archive
Fund, 2004

Thomas Brock 1847–1922

1968.0007.0126
Bust of Douglas Galton (1822–1899),
1902
Marble
78.9 × 65 × 38cm
Presented as part of the Gascoigne
Bequest, 1968

Alfred Bromley 1817–c.1865)

1972.0037.0004
Bust of Richard Hobson (1795–1868),
1857
Marble
83.8 × 57 × 44cm
Presented by United Leeds
Hospitals, 1972

1972.0003.T
Bust of James Kitson (1835–1911),

*c.*1865
Marble
76.2 × 47 × 34cm
Presented by United Leeds
Hospitals, 1972

Ralph Brown b.1928

1958.0009.0001
Tragic Group, 1953
Bronze
45.5 × 47.5 × 20cm
Purchased from the artist by the
LACF with the aid of a grant from the
Corporation Fund, 1958

1957.0027
Mother and Child, 1954
Bronze
100 × 42 × 61cm
Purchased with the aid of a grant from
the Corporation Fund, 1957

1958.0010.0001

Running Girl with Wheel, 1954
Bronze
25 × 30.5 × 15cm
Purchased from the artist by the
LACF with the aid of a grant from the
Corporation Fund, 1958

George Bullock 1777–1818

1981.0041
Portrait of Henry Blundell, 1801
Coloured wax and gilded plaster
45.5 × 39 × 11.5cm
Purchased with the aid of a grant from
the V&A Purchase Grant Fund, 1981

2000.0026.T
Bust of William Hey (1736–1819), 1816
Plaster
67 × 49 × 32cm
Acquisition source unknown

John Bunting 1927–2002 A

2005.0018
Standing Woman, 1949
Oak wood
41.5 × 10.7 × 9cm
Purchased through the HMI Archive
Fund, 2004

2005.0019
Standing Woman, 1949
Bronze
42.5 × 16.9 × 7.8cm
Purchased through the HMI Archive
Fund, 2004

2005.0017
Man Looking to Heaven, 1955
Painted and gilded clay
13.5 × 11 × 11cm
Purchased through the HMI Archive
Fund, 2004

Laurence Burt b.1925

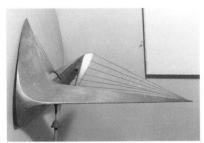

1957.0030
Decorative Sculpture, 1957
Bronze and string
106.5 × 64.5 × 52cm
Purchased 1957

2005.0006
Helmet, 1974
Iron
31 × 8 × 11cm
Presented by the artist, 2003

Reg Butler 1913–1981   A

1957.0006.0001
Girl, 1956
Bronze
147.3 × 46 × 37cm
Purchased by the LACF, 1957

Alexander Calder 1898–1976

2000.0082
Maquette for a Mobile, 1939
Painted metal, wood, wire and string
105 × 120 × 120cm
Purchased with the aid of grants from
the HLF, the NACF, MLA/V&A Purchase
Grant Fund and the HMF, 2000

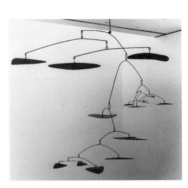

1963.0014.0001
Chicago Black, 1948
Sheet aluminium and painted steel
H.122cm
Purchased from the artist by the LACF,
1963

Antonio Canova 1757–1822   A

1959.0021.0003
Venus, 1817–20
Marble
177 × 52 × 70cm
Presented by Mrs Dorothy Una
McGrigor-Phillips, 1959

Anonymous
after Antonio Canova

2000.0052.T
**Princess Marie Pauline Borghese
(1780–1825) as Venus Victrix,** mid-19th
century (original 1804–8)
Marble
42.5 × 71.8 × 21cm
Acquisition source unknown

Anthony Caro b.1924   D

1987.0040
Smiling Head III (Smiling Woman),
1956
Bronze
32 × 19 × 18cm
Purchased with the aid of a grant from
the V&A Purchase Grant Fund, 1987

1996.0051
Emma Books, 1977–8
Rusted and varnished steel
132 × 160 × 61cm
Presented by the artist, 1996

1982.0038.0001
National Grid, 1978–9
Steel and sheet steel
133.5 × 183 × 129cm
Purchased from the artist by the
LACF to mark the opening of the new
extension to Leeds City Art Gallery,
with the aid of a grant from the V&A
Purchase Grant Fund, 1982

Andrew Carpenter 1677–1737

1887.0071
Statue of Anne I (1665–1714), 1712
Marble
H.198cm
Presented by Frederick Milner, 1887

Albert-Ernest Carrier-Belleuse
1824–1887

1966.0001L
La Liseuse [The Reader], 1887
Bronze and ivory
59.5 × 16 × 18cm

Presented anonymously to the LACF,
1966

Jean Cavalier c.1640–1707

1980.0027
Charles II (1630–1685) on Horseback,
1684
Ivory
15.3 × 12.5 × 3cm
Purchased with the aid of grants from
the V&A Purchase Grant Fund and the
NACF, 1980

Hermon Cawthra 1886–1972   A

1970.0013.0001A
**Model of the Sculpture on Leeds Civic
Hall: Putto with a Goat,** 1933
Bronze
19 × 14 × 13.5cm
Presented by Vincent Harris through
Leeds Civic Hall, 1970

1970.0013.0001B
**Model of the Sculpture on Leeds Civic
Hall: Putto with a Turkey,** 1933
Bronze
19 × 14 × 13.5cm
Presented by Vincent Harris through
Leeds Civic Hall, 1970

Attributed to Hermon Cawthra

2003.0046
Architectural Panel: Beach Scene,
c.1910s
Stone
48.8 × 34.5 × 8cm
Acquisition source unknown

Helen Chadwick 1953–1996 A

2003.0019
Menstrual Piece, 1976
Mixed media
117 × 83 × 7cm
Presented by the Helen Chadwick
Estate, 2003

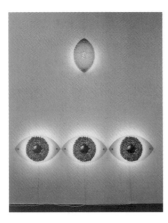

2004.0010
Eat Me, 1991
Cibachrome prints, glass, aluminium
and electrical apparatus
Overall: 278 × 253 × 15cm
Purchased from the Helen Chadwick
Estate with the aid of grants from the
NACF and the MLA/V&A Purchase
Grant Fund, 2003

Lynn Chadwick 1914–2003

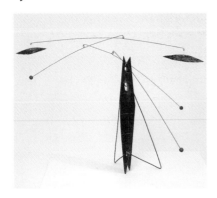

1992.0019
Mobile, 1950
Iron rods, slate and brass

Diam. 45cm
Purchased through the HMI Archive
Fund, 1992

Anonymous after Francis Chantrey
1781–1841

2000.0032.T
Bust of James Watt (1736–1819), late-
19th century (original 1841)
Plaster
67 × 46 × 34cm
Acquisition source unknown

Siegfried Charoux 1896–1967

1996.0037
Maquette for The Neighbours, 1957–9
Bronze and wood
20 × 32 × 19.5cm
Presented by the Hon. David Astor,
1996

Alexandre-Louis-Marie Charpentier
1856–1909

1899.0411.0001
The Singer [La Chanteuse], 1897–9
Gilt bronze
8 × 14.5 × 0.5cm
Purchased 1899

1899.0411.0002
**Girl Playing the Violin [La Fille au
Violin],** 1897–9
Gilt bronze
8 × 14.5 × 0.5cm
Purchased 1899

John Cheere 1709–1787

1922.0003.T
**Bust of Marcus Tullius Cicero (106–43
BC),** c.1754
Painted plaster
H.66cm
Presented by Lord Halifax, 1922

1922.0004.T
**Bust of Lucius Annaeus Seneca
(5 BC–65 AD),** c.1754
Painted plaster
H.66cm
Presented by Lord Halifax, 1922

1922.0005.T
**Bust of Quintus Horatius Flaccus
[Horace] (65–8 BC),** *c.*1754
Painted plaster
H.66cm
Presented by Lord Halifax, 1922

Geoffrey Clarke b.1924   A

1995.0021
Head, *c.*1953
Iron and stone
40 × 27 × 17cm
Purchased through the HMI Archive
Fund, 1995

Isaac Cooke 1846–1922

1943.0015
**Medallion Portrait of Mary Theresa
Odell** (*fl.*1913–1945), 1913
Bronze
Diam. 8cm
Presented by Jacob Simon, 1982

Stephen Cox b.1946   A D

1995.0003
Four Pietra Serena Wedges, 1979
Pietra Serena sandstone
Overall: 24 × 130 × 24cm
Presented by the artist via the HMF,
1995

1994.0038 A–F
Colour Crucibles (Cluster II), 1980
Stone and pigment
Trefoil × 2: 24 × 15.5 × 16cm
Spiral × 2: 17 × 10.5 × 12.5cm
Bar × 2: 15.5 × 16 × 19cm
Presented by the artist via the HMF,
1995

1994.0039.0001–0003
Tondo: Disk I, Disk II, Disk III, 1980
Bath stone
32 × 38 × 9.5cm
32 × 34 × 11cm
32 × 44 × 11cm
Presented by the artist via the HMF,
1995

1995.0005
Majolica Dish, 1981
Tin glazed earthenware
Diam. 54cm
Presented by the artist via the HMF,
1995

1987.0058
Tanmatras, 1985
Black granite
Variable dimensions
Purchased from the artist with the aid
of a grant from the HMF, 1987

1994.0051
Bowl XIII, 1989
Black Porphyry stone
15.5 × 8.4 × 8.4cm
Presented by the artist via the HMF,
1995

Tony Cragg b.1949   D

1982.0053
Postcard Flag (Union Jack), 1981
Plastic
300 × 440 × 10cm
Presented by the CAS, 1982

Hubert Dalwood 1924–1976   A

1960.0013.0001
Icon, 1958
Aluminium
78 × 141 × 32cm
Purchased by the LACF, 1960

1960.0012.0001
Object-Open Square, 1959
Aluminium
34 × 41 × 11.5cm
Presented anonymously to the LACF, 1960

1982.0048
Flag, 1962
Aluminium
76 × 38 × 20.5cm
Presented by Mrs Sara Gilchrist, 1982

1967.0002.L
Maquette for a Frieze at the Front of Leeds City Art Gallery, 1967
Aluminium
20.5 × 141.5 × 5cm
Gift of Arts Council England, 2006

2002.0057
Maquette for the Public Sculpture at the Office of National Statistics, Tredegar Park, Newport, Gwent, c.1972
Silver painted wood
60.5 × 30 × 59cm
Presented by Caroline and Kevin Ireland, 2002

2002.0056
Maquette for Column Landscape II, c.1970
Varnished plaster
10.5 × 13.5 × 9.7cm
Presented by Caroline and Kevin Ireland, 2002

2002.0055
Maquette for the Public Sculpture at the Haymarket Shopping Centre and Haymarket Theatre, Leicester, 1974
Brown painted wood
59.3 × 36.5 × 33.5cm
Presented by Caroline and Kevin Ireland, 2002

2002.0058
Maquette for the Public Sculpture at the Haymarket Shopping Centre and Haymarket Theatre, Leicester, 1974
Brown painted wood
26.7 × 15 × 17.7cm
Presented by Caroline and Kevin Ireland, 2002

2002.0043
Table I, 1976
Wood and plaster
81 × 78 × 65cm

Presented by Caroline and Kevin
Ireland, 2002

2002.0054
Maquette for Kangra II, 1976
Terrosa Ferrata
7.2 × 17.8 × 16.3cm
Presented by Caroline and Kevin
Ireland, 2002

Pierre-Jean David d'Angers
1788–1856

1924.0023
**Medallion Portrait of Jean-Pierre
Béranger (1780–1857)**, 1830
Bronze
Diam. 13.8cm
Bequeathed by A. Saunders, 1923

Frances Darlington 1880–1939

1906.0097
The Little Sea Maiden, 1905
Plaster
77.5 × 64 × 50.5cm
Purchased 1906

Grenville Davey b.1961   A D

1996.0052
(gold) Table, 1991
MDF and oak veneer
128.5 × 225.5 × 128.5cm
Gift of the CAS, 1996

John Warren Davis b.1919

1957.0005.0001
Standing Figure, 1957
Bronze
98 × 32.6 × 25.5cm
Purchased from the artist by the LACF,
1957

John Davies b.1946

2005.0488
Three Heads No.21, 1978
Wood, metal and plaster
25.5 × 12.5 × 4.3cm
Given by Dasha Shenkman through the
CAS, 2005

Richard Deacon b.1949   D

1997.0020.0005 *3*
Maquette for Nobody Here But Us,
1990
MDF, hardboard, paper, paint and
pencil
26 × 37 × 30cm
Purchased from the artist through the
HMI Archive Fund, 1997

1997.0020.0004
Maquette for Nobody Here But Us,
1990
MDF and paint
31 × 37 × 25cm
Purchased from the artist through the
HMI Archive Fund, 1997

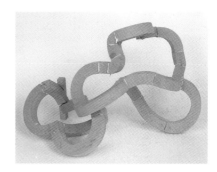

1997.0020.0002 *5*
Maquette for Nobody Here But Us,
1990
MDF and pencil
28.2 × 42 × 24.5cm
Purchased from the artist through the
HMI Archive Fund, 1997

1997.0020.0001
Maquette for Almost Beautiful, 1994
Polyester resin filler
10.8 × 22 × 6cm
Purchased from the artist through the
HMI Archive Fund, 1997

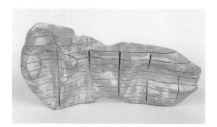

1997.0020.0001
Maquette for Almost Beautiful, 1994
MDF and pencil
10.2 × 35.5 × 18cm
Purchased from the artist, 1997

Alexis Decaix *fl.*1794–1803

1967.0024.0038.0001 & 0002
Pair of Greyhounds, *c.*1802
(1 illustrated)
Bronze and brass
15 × 19 × 70cm
Bequeathed by Mrs Dorothy Una
McGrigor-Phillips, 1967

Jan Claudius de Cock 1667–1735

1943.0008
Bust of a Boy, 1704
Marble
35.6 × 27 × 25cm
Purchased 1943

William Reid Dick 1879–1961

1987.0025
Maquette for Two Greyhounds, 1927
Plaster
18.5 × 10.5 × 20.5cm
Presented by Mrs Mary Hart and Mrs
Anne Benton through the Fine Art
Society, 1987

1933.0001.T
Bust of George V (1865–1936), 1932
Marble
63 × 68 × 32cm
Presented by R. H. Blackburn, 1933

Frank Dobson 1886–1963   A

1936.0031
**Bust of Margaret Rawlings, Lady
Barlow (1906–1996),** *c.*1936
Bronze
55 × 53 × 55cm
Purchased with the aid of grants from
the Corporation Fund and the Board of
Education, 1936

2002.0041
First Portrait of Ann Dobson (b.1928),
1940
Plaster
25.5 × 24 × 21.5cm
Acquisition source unknown

2005.0487
Model for The Fount, 1947–48
Patinated plaster
165 × 49 × 65cm
Purchased with the aid of a grant from
the NACF, 2005

Jacqueline Donachie b.1969

2004.0016.T
In the Arms of Strangers, 2001
Judo crash mats, CD, CD player and
speakers
Variable dimensions
Commissioned from the artist, 2001

Harold James Dow 1902–1967

1925.0109
Owl, *c.*1920
Marble
168 × 26 × 26.5cm
Presented by Oliver Swithenbank, 1925

Alfred Drury 1858–1944   A

1895.0069
Circe, 1893
Bronze
261 × 108 × 108cm
Purchased with the aid of a grant from
the Corporation Fund, 1895

Chris Drury b.1948

1987.0046
Medicine Wheel, 1982–3
Mixed media
Diam. 221.5cm
Presented by the artist, 1987

Marcel Duchamp 1887–1968

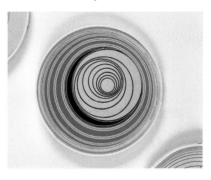

1987.0038
Rotoreliefs, 1935 (partial view)
Mixed media
93 × 94 × 21cm
Purchased 1987

Anonymous after Louis-Marie-Charles-Henri Dupaty 1771–1825

1968.0007.0661
The Wounded Philoctetes, mid 19th-
century (original 1810)
Marble
142 × 59 × 99cm
Presented as part of the Gascoigne
Bequest, 1968

Thomas Earle 1810–1876

1972.0037.0005
Bust of Thomas Pridgin Teale (1801–1867), 1867
Marble
69.9 × 51 × 25cm
Presented by United Leeds Hospitals,
1972

Anthony Earnshaw 1924–2001

1987.0035
Agony in the Garden, 1978
Mixed media
49.5 × 44.1 × 8.5cm
Purchased from the artist with the
aid of a grant from the V&A Purchase
Grant Fund, 1987

1987.0034
Crusoe's Dream, 1979
Mixed media
72.8 × 57.3 × 12cm
Purchased from the artist, 1987

1987.0068
Raider's Bread, 1979
Mixed media
12 × 34 × 24cm
Purchased from the artist by a group of subscribers, 1987

Jacob Epstein 1880–1959 A D

1968.0006.0007
Baby Asleep, 1904
Bronze
12 × 11 × 18cm
Presented by Ludmilla Mlada, 1968

1988.0050
Baby Asleep, 1904
Plaster
12 × 11 × 18cm
Presented by Beth Lipkin, 1988

1988.0051
Baby Asleep, 1904
Wax
12 × 11 × 18cm
Presented by Beth Lipkin, 1988

1942.0017
Bust of Mary McEvoy, 1910
Bronze
44.5 × 38 × 19cm
Purchased with the aid of a grant from the Corporation Fund, 1942

1983.0050
Maternity, 1910
Hopton Wood stone
203 × 91 × 46cm
Purchased with the aid of grants from the NACF, the NHMF and various private benefactors, 1983

1937.0003
Nan Condron, c.1911
Wax
6 × 9 × 11cm
Acquisition source unknown

1942.0011
Bust of Lady Isobella Augusta Gregory (1859–1932), 1911
Bronze
38 × 32.5 × 25.5cm
Purchased with the aid of a grant from the Corporation Fund, 1942

1987.0056.0001
Bust of Marie Rankin, 1911
Bronze
36.5 × 31 × 24cm
Purchased with the aid of a grant from the HMF, 1987

1931.0019
Bust of Jacob Kramer (1892–1962),
1921
Bronze
64 × 54 × 25cm
Presented by the LACF, 1931

1950.0033
Rose, *c.*1932
Bronze
37.5 × 21 × 23cm
Purchased 1950

1983.0041.0001
Deirdre (First Portrait with Arms),
1941
Bronze
64 × 46 × 46cm
Presented anonymously to LACF, 1983

1942.0010
Peggy Jean Laughing, 1921
Bronze
23.5 × 21 × 23cm
Purchased with the aid of a grant from
the Corporation Fund, 1942

1950.0032
Lydia Laughing, 1933
Bronze
41 × 23.5 × 25cm
Purchased with the aid of a grant from
the Corporation Fund, 1950

1993.0045.0001
Bust of George Black (1903–1987),
1942
Bronze
63 × 54 × 38cm
Bequeathed by Mrs George Black
through the LACF, 1993

1996.0061
Peggy Jean (Sick Child), 1928
Bronze
36 × 50 × 56cm
Presented by Mrs Vivienne Haskell
in memory of her husband Arnold
Haskell, 1996

1937.0031
Elsa, 1936
Bronze
36 × 24 × 28cm
Purchased 1937

1973.0035.0001
Victor, 1949
Bronze
26 × 17 × 20cm
Bequeathed by Jocelyn Horner to the
LACF, 1973

David Evans 1883–1959

1933.0026
Bust of John Galsworthy (1867–1933), 1928
Bronze
54 × 18.5 × 22cm
Presented by Charles Carpenter, 1933

Garth Evans b.1934

2003.0025
Wedge II, 1979
Pine wood and adhesives
112 × 140 × 22.8cm
Presented by the artist, 2003

John Farnham b.1942   D

1983.0066.0001
Crossed Fingers, 1974
Plaster
18.5 × 11.5 × 16cm
Presented by the artist, 1983

1984.0018
Broken Heart, 1980
Soapstone
28.2 × 53 × 27cm
Purchased from the artist with the aid of a grant from the V&A Purchase Grant Fund, 1984

Henry Charles Fehr 1867–1940

2002.0059
Head of Victory from the Leeds War Memorial, 1922
Bronze
31.5 × 28.5 × 26cm
Transferred from Leeds City Council's Parks and Countryside Division, 1990

Ian Hamilton Finlay
1925–2006   A

1996.0057
Wordsworth Wadsworth, c.1977
Portland stone
29.5 × 49.5 × 5cm
Presented by Ronnie Duncan, 1996

Barry Flanagan b.1941

1980.0016
Clay Figure, 1975
Impacted clay and brown Hornton stone
49 × 25 × 27cm
Purchased with the aid of a grant from the V&A Purchase Grant Fund, 1980

1982.0027
The Cricketer, 1982
Bronze
158 × 60.5 × 39.3cm
Purchased 1982

John Flaxman 1755–1826   D

1983.0021
Charity, c.1816
Plaster
110.5 × 52 × 15cm
Presented by the Wellcome Institute, 1983

Arthur Fleischmann
1896–1990   A

1994.0036
Maquette for the Lockheed Fountain 'Miranda', 1951
Gilded terracotta
23.2 × 13.3 × 7cm
Purchased through the HMI Archive Fund, 1994

1994.0037
Maquette for the Lockheed Fountain 'Miranda', 1951
Gilded terracotta
26.5 × 15 × 8cm
Purchased through the HMI Archive Fund, 1994

Winslow Foot   b.1939

1965.0001.L
Three by Fifteen, c.1960
Painted chipboard and aluminium
66.6 × 57.9 × 5 cm
Presented to the LACF by Stanley Burton, 1966

1966.0023.0001
Wirefive, c.1965
Steel rods on painted chipboard
107.7 × 98 × 50cm
Purchased by the LACF, 1966

Edward Onslow Ford   1852–1901

1925.0551.0001
Mother and Child, 1879
Terracotta
38 × 11.5 × 18.5cm
Presented by Mrs S. Ingham, 1923–4

1925.0551.0002
Mother and Child, 1879
Terracotta
38 × 1.5 × 13.5cm
Presented by Mrs S. Ingham, 1923–4

George Frampton   1860–1928   A

2001.0068

St. Christina, 1889–93
Plaster with sepia wash, mounted in an oak frame made by the artist
43.2 × 24 × 6cm
Purchased with the aid of a grant from the MLA/V&A Purchase Grant Fund, 2001

George Fullard   1923–1973   A

1999.0019
Captive, 1964
Mixed media
72 × 46.5 × 13.5cm
Purchased with the aid of a grant from the V&A Purchase Grant Fund, 1999

Hamish Fulton   b.1946

1983.0033.0001
Arran Hilltops, 1978
2 photographs on paper
80 × 87.5cm
Purchased 1980

Naum Gabo 1880–1977

1989.0022
Construction in Space: Soaring, 1930
Brass, plexiglass and wood
112 × 77 × 71cm
Accepted by HM Government in Lieu
of Inheritance Tax and allocated to
Leeds City Council for display at Leeds
City Art Gallery, 1989

Anya Gallaccio b.1963

1994.0030
Six Dozen Red Roses, 1992
Dried roses and card
4.2 × 12 × 15cm
Purchased through the HMI Archive
Fund, 1994

1994.0029
Couverture, 1994

Silkscreen on paper, aluminium,
chocolate and cocoa butter
20.5 × 18.5 × 18.5cm
Purchased through the HMI Archive
Fund, 1994

Henri Gaudier-Brzeska
1891–1915   A D

1943.0019
The Wrestler, 1912
Lead
64.5 × 29.4 × 37.5cm
Purchased with the aid of a grant from
the Board of Education, 1943

1935.0019
Odalisque (Man and Woman), 1912–13
Alabaster
20.7 × 34.7 × 5.7cm
Purchased with the aid of a grant from
the Board of Education, 1935

1943.0015
Bust of Horace Brodzky (1885–1969),
1913
Bronze
64.5 × 56 × 34.5cm

Purchased with the aid of the Harding
Bequest Fund, 1943

Alfred Horace Gerrard
1899–1998   A

2003.0030
**Bust of Winifred Monnington (née
Knights) (1899–1947),** c.1926–7
Bronze
35.7 × 14 × 18cm
Presented by Karen Gerrard, 2003

2003.0029.0001
**Maquette for The North Wind
(possibly for that at St. James' Park
Underground Station, 55 Broadway,
London),** c.1928
Portland stone
14.7 × 24.7 × 12.2cm
Purchased through the HMI Archive
Fund, 2003

2003.0029.0002
**Maquette for The North Wind
(possibly for that at St. James' Park
Underground Station, 55 Broadway,
London),** c.1928
Portland stone
17 × 25.2 × 12cm

Purchased through the HMI Archive
Fund, 2003

2003.0029.0003
**Maquette for The North Wind
(possibly for that at St. James' Park
Underground Station, 55 Broadway,
London),** *c.*1928
Portland stone
25.2 × 14.3 × 12.5cm
Purchased through the HMI Archive
Fund, 2003

2003.0031
Maquette for Dance, *c.*1960
Portland stone
25.2 × 14.3 × 12.5cm
Purchased through the HMI Archive
Fund, 2003

Anonymous after Giambologna

2001.0003.T
Mercury, 19th century (original 1564)
Bronze
77 × 36 × 26cm
Acquisition source unknown

Alfred Gilbert 1854–1934   A D

1925.0334.0001
Perseus Arming, 1882 (cast 1910)
Bronze
76.2 × 40.5 × 26cm
Bequeathed by Sam Wilson, 1925

1925.0209
**The Sam Wilson Chimneypiece
(A Dream of Joy During a Sleep of
Sorrow),** *c.*1908–14
Bronze
351 × 213.8 × 94.6cm
Bequeathed by Sam Wilson, 1925

1937.0003.0011
Maquette for the Head of Icarus, *c.*1884
Plaster and wax
7 × 4.5 × 5.5cm
Presented by Sigismund Goetze
through the NACF, 1937

1937.0003.0023
**Maquette for the Sir William Lawrence
Gold Annual Award Medal,** *c.*1897
Lead
Diam. 7.5 cm
Presented by Sigismund Goetze
through the NACF, 1937

1937.0003.0001–0009
**9 Maquettes for the Sam Wilson
Chimneypiece,** *c.*1908–14
(1 illustrated)
Plaster and shellac
Min. 7.5cm, max. 85cm
Presented by Sigismund Goetze
through the NACF, 1937

1937.0003.0014
**Maquette for the Double Panel of
Foliage for the Crown on the Figure of
Charity on the Alexandria Memorial,**
*c.*1932
Bronzed plaster
16 × 11.5 × 1.5cm
Presented by Sigismund Goetze
through the NACF, 1937

1937.0003.0012
Maquette for the Stamp of the O.W. Paper Art Company Ltd., undated
Bronzed plaster
Diam. 4.7cm
Presented by Sigismund Goetze through the NACF, 1937

1937.0003.0013
Maquette for an Octagonal Plaque, undated
Gilded plaster
8 × 7 × 1cm
Presented by Sigismund Goetze through the NACF, 1937

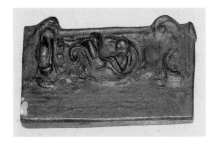

1937.0003.0015
Maquette for a Panel with a Seated Figure, undated
Painted plaster
10 × 7 × 2cm
Presented by Sigismund Goetze through the NACF, 1937

1937.0003.0016–0018
Maquette for a Key Bow with a Cupid Whispering to a Seated Girl: three sketches for the Central Group, undated
Plaster
Min. 1.6, max: 8.4cm
Presented by Sigismund Goetze through the NACF, 1937

1937.0003.0019
Maquette for a Key Bow (or Finial) with an Allegory of Love, undated
Bronzed plaster
6 × 4.6 × 2cm
Presented by Sigismund Goetze through the NACF, 1937

1937.0003.0020
Maquette for a Pendant with the Dead Christ Sustained by Two Angels, undated
Bronzed plaster
5.8 × 4.7 × 2cm

Presented by Sigismund Goetze through the NACF, 1937

1937.0003.0021
Maquette for a Pendant with an Arabesque Escutcheon, undated
Bronzed plaster
7.5 × 7 × 2cm
Presented by Sigismund Goetze through the NACF, 1937

1937.0003.0022
Maquette for a Pendant with Two Figures Hanging Over the Figure of a Child, undated
Plaster
9.5 × 5 × 2.5 cm
Presented by Sigismund Goetze through the NACF, 1937

Eric Gill 1882–1940   A D

1995.0029
Mother and Child, 1910

Portland stone
62.2 × 20.3 × 17.1cm
Purchased with the aid of grants from
the NHMF, the V&A Purchase Grant
Fund and the Pilgrim Trust, 1995

See also **Kindersley, David**

Andy Goldsworthy b.1956   A D

1991.43
32 Leafworks, 1988–89
Leaves: London plane, chestnut,
sycamore and beech
Min: 8cm, max: 188cm
Purchased through the HMF with the
aid of a grant from the V&A Purchase
Grant Fund, 1991

Antony Gormley b.1950   A D

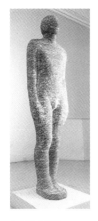

1987.0036
Maquette for the Leeds Brick Man,
1986
Fired clay, cement and fibreglass
195 × 51 × 34cm
Purchased with the aid of a grant from
the V&A Purchase Grant Fund, 1987

1992.0059
Earth Above Ground, 1986
Lead, fibreglass, plaster and air
198 × 69 × 34.5cm
Presented by the CAS, 1992

Joseph Gott 1786–1860   A

1970.0023
**Venus Dissuading Adonis from the
Chase,** 1824
Terracotta
54.5 × 32 × 32cm
Purchased with the aid of a grant from
the Corporation Fund, 1970

1982.0019
The Penitent Magdalene, 1824
Terracotta
19 × 10.5 × 12.5cm
Purchased 1982

1972.0008
**Three Nymphs Carrying Cupid in
Triumph,** 1825
Marble
94 × 42 × 57cm
Purchased with the aid of a grant from
the Corporation Fund, 1972

1971.0029
Maquette for A Pastoral Apollo, 1827
Terracotta
16 × 10 × 12cm
Purchased with the aid of a grant from
the Corporation Fund, 1971

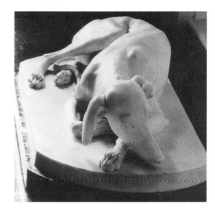

1971.0030
Greyhound, 1827
Marble
14 × 28 × 55cm
Purchased with the aid of a grant from
the Corporation Fund, 1971

1928.0001
**Bust of Elizabeth Goodman Banks
(1781–1853),** 1828
Marble
44.5 × 50 × 24cm
Presented by Mrs E.C. Banks, 1928

1928.0002
Bust of Eros, 1828
Marble
72.5 × 20 × 22cm
Presented by Mrs E.C. Banks, 1928

1928.0003
Bust of George Banks (1777–1843),
1828
Marble
72.5 × 54 × 31cm
Presented by Mrs E.C. Banks, 1928

1928.0003.0001
George Banks (1777–1843), Seated,
1828
Marble
55.5 × 61 × 24cm
Presented by Mrs E.C. Banks, 1928

1971.0009
**Maquette for Greek Boxer Awaiting his
Turn,** 1828
Terracotta
19 × 11 × 17cm
Purchased with the aid of a grant from
the Corporation Fund, 1971

1973.0008
**Maquette for George Banks (1777–
1843), Seated,** 1828
Plaster
20 × 10 × 23cm
Purchased 1973

1973.0009
**Maquette for Elizabeth Goodman
Banks (1781–1853), Seated,** 1828
Plaster
18 × 20 × 11.5cm
Purchased with the aid of a grant from
the Corporation Fund, 1973

1973.0010
**Bust of Elizabeth Goodman Banks
(1781–1853),** 1828
Plaster
16 × 11 × 6.5cm
Purchased with the aid of a grant from
the Corporation Fund, 1973

2000.0021.T
Bust of Benjamin Gott (1762–1840),
1828
Marble
68 × 55 × 30cm
Transferred from Leeds City Museum,
1971

2000.0051.T
Bust of Benjamin Gott (1762–1840),
1828–9
Marble
68 × 55 × 30cm
Transferred from Leeds City Museum,
1971

1928.0002.0001
Bust of a Satyr, 1829
Marble
53.3 × 32 × 18cm
Presented by Mrs E.C. Banks, 1928

1977.0015.0002
Maquette for Margaret Gott (1822–
1883) as a Babe in the Wood, 1829
Terracotta
7 × 18 × 8cm
Purchased with the aid of a grant from
the V&A Purchase Grant Fund, 1977

1977.0015.0002
Maquette for Jane Gott (b.1825) as a
Babe in the Wood, 1829
Terracotta
8.4 × 18 × 8cm
Purchased with the aid of a grant from
the V&A Purchase Grant Fund, 1977

1928.0003.0002
Metobus and Camilla, 1830
Marble
90 × 71cm
Presented by Mrs E.C. Banks, 1928

1967.0001.0005
Medallion Portrait of Mrs Elizabeth
Allan (née Gott) (1794–1880), 1834
Marble
Diam. 17cm
Purchased with the aid of a grant from
the Corporation Fund, 1967

1972.0030
Nymph and Greyhound, 1834

Marble
33.5 × 26 × 16cm
Presented by Mr. and Mrs B.J.
Friedman, 1972

2000.0013.T
Medallion Portrait of Mrs Mary
Brooke (née Gott) (1802–1882), 1834
Marble
Diam. 16.4cm
Acquisition source unknown

2005.0490
Bust of John Gott (1791–1867), 1834–5
Marble
62 × 49 × 30cm
Acquisition source unknown

2005.0489
Bust of William Gott (1797–1863),
1834–5
Marble
73 × 49 × 28cm
Acquisition source unknown

1967.0001.0002
Medallion Portrait of Mrs Elizabeth Gott (née Rhodes) (1767–1857), 1835
Marble
Diam. 17cm
Purchased with the aid of a grant from the Corporation Fund, 1967

1967.0001.0003
Medallion Portrait of Mrs Margaret Gott (née Ewart) (1767–1857), 1835
Marble
Diam. 17cm
Purchased with the aid of a grant from the Corporation Fund, 1967

1967.0001.0004
Medallion Portrait of Benjamin Gott (1762–1840), 1835
Marble
Diam. 17cm
Purchased with the aid of a grant from the Corporation Fund, 1967

2005.0505
Cupid and Psyche, 1835
Marble
70 × 157cm
Transferred from Armley House by the Parks Department, 1972

1967.0001.0005
Medallion Portrait of Harriet Gott (1795–1883), 1836
Marble
Diam. 17cm
Purchased with the aid of a grant from the Corporation Fund, 1967

Joseph Gott 1786–1860
after Antonio Canova

1896.0053
Bust of Napoleon I (1769–1821), 1830s
(original c.1803)
Marble
57.3 × 33 × 26cm
Presented by Ernest W. Beckett, Lord Grimthorpe, 1896

Attributed to Caspar Gras
1585–1674

1944.0009
Lion Attacking a Horse, late 17th century
Bronze
25.5 × 30.5 × 18.5cm
Purchased 1944

Emilio Greco 1913–1995

1954.0054.0001
Female Figure, c.1949
Bronze
86 × 29 × 40cm
Purchased by the LACF, 1954

Brian Griffiths b.1968

Awaiting accession no.
Return of Enos, 2000

Carpet, cardboard and tape
230 × 90 × 40cm
Presented by the CAS, 2005

Martin Grose b.1933

1976.0045.0003
Wedding Portrait, 1970
Perspex, wood, plaster, paint and glass
122.5 × 82.5 × 15cm
Presented by Arthur Haigh, 1976

Alfred Hardiman 1891–1949   A

2005.0510
Bust of Thomas Ashby (1874–1931),
1922
Bronze
44 × 20.5 × 20.5cm
Presented by Janis Hardiman, 2003

2005.0511

**Two maquettes for Knights for the
Battle of Britain Altar at Westminster
Abbey,** 1947
Plaster
56 × 17 × 10cm and 55.5 × 18 × 11cm
Presented by Janis Hardiman, 2003

Barry Hart c.1890–1953

2004.0008
Torso, 1930
Alabaster
102 × 26 × 17cm
Purchased with the aid of grants from
the MLA/V&A Purchase Grant Fund
and the LACF, 2003

Mark Harvey b.1913

1956.0026
**Bust of T. Edmund Harvey (fl.1897–
1949),** 1950
Bronze
23 × 16cm
Presented by the Harvey Family, 1956

Donald Hastings 1900–1938   A

2002.0091
Bust of a Man, c.1934
Glazed ceramic
25.4 × 18 × 24.5cm
Presented by Eveline and Julian
Hastings, 2002

Barbara Hepworth
1903–1975   A D

1990.0042
Single Form, 1937
Holly wood
89.9 × 28 × 17.6cm
Purchased with the aid of grants from
the HMF and the NHMF, 1990

1943.0009
Conicoid, 1939
Teak wood
20.4 × 20 × 20cm
Purchased 1943

2002.0096
Maquette 'C' for the Sculpture at Waterloo Bridge, London, 1947
Plaster
16 × 8 × 11cm
Presented by Alan Bowness, 2002

1968.0001
Hieroglyph, 1953
Ancaster stone
101.8 × 86 × 45cm
Presented by the artist, 1968

1958.0008.0001
Configuration (Phira), 1955
Scented Guarea wood
68 × 68 × 64cm
Purchased by the LACF, 1958

1967.0029.0001
Dual Form, 1965
Bronze
192.5 × 141 × 68cm
Purchased from the artist by the LACF, 1967

Gertrude Hermes   1901–1983   A

2000.0016
Two in One, 1937–9
China clay
11 × 8 × 2.5cm
Presented by Judith Russell, 2000

2000.0073
Bust of the Reverend Conrad Noel (1896–1942), 1939
Plaster and shellac
30.4 × 22.5 × 23cm
Presented by Judith Russell and Simon Hughes-Stanton in memory of Gertrude Hermes, 2000

2000.0074
Bust of Sir Michael Tippett (1905–1998), 1966
Plaster
35.5 × 20.3 × 25.4cm
Presented by Judith Russell and Simon Hughes-Stanton in memory of Gertrude Hermes, 2000

Attributed to Christopher Hewetson
1739–1799

1968.0007.0123

Bust of Sir Thomas Gascoigne (1744–1810), 1778
Bronze
50.8 × 40 × 24cm
Presented as part of the Gascoigne Bequest, 1968

1968.0007.0124
Bust of Mrs Martha Swinburne (née Baker) (c.1767–d.1809), 1779
Bronze
48.2 × 33 × 26cm
Presented as part of the Gascoigne Bequest, 1968

1968.0007.0125
Bust of Henry Swinburne (1743–1803), 1779
Bronze
53.3 × 38 × 25cm
Presented as part of the Gascoigne Bequest, 1968

Anthony Hill b.1930

2003.0023
Maquette for a Relief Mural for the Sixth Congress of the International Union of Architects, South Bank, London, 1961
Aluminium, plastic and chipboard
18.5 × 122 × 2.7cm
Purchased from the artist with the aid

of grants from the MLA/V&A Purchase Grant Fund and the NACF, 2003

Susan Hiller b.1940

1988.0031
Monument 1980–1: Colonial Version, 1980–1
Bench, wall plaques and sound
Variable dimensions
Purchased by the LACF, 1988

Phill Hopkins b.1961   D

1992.0004
I Fall to Pieces, 1991
Wire mesh, wastepaper basket and metal
30 × 30.8 × 30.8 cm
Purchased 1992

Jocelyn Horner 1902–1973   A

1949.0010
Annunciation, 1949
Tinted plaster
52 × 15 × 24cm
Purchased 1949

1972.0040.0001
The Hands of Sir John Barbirolli (1899–1970), 1972
Bronze
145 × 121 × 54.5cm
Purchased by the LACF, 1972

John Hoskin 1921–1990   A D

1994.0033
Standing Figure, 1963
Oxidised steel
99 × 123 × 24cm
Purchased through the HMI Archive Fund, 1994

2000.0084
Untitled, c.1965
Iron
69 × 34 × 15.5cm
Presented by Sara Hicks in memory of Bernard Schottlander, 1999

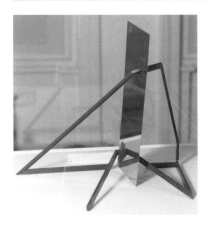

1994.0034
Maquette for Untitled, *c.*1974
Aluminium and steel
39.5 × 26.5 × 47cm
Purchased through the HMI Archive
Fund, 1994

1994.0035
Maquette for Bronze Grid with Red,
1985
Bronze and slate
46 × 12.7 × 10.2cm
Purchased through the HMI Archive
Fund, 1994

Charles Sargeant Jagger
1885–1934   A D

1998.0008.0001
**Maquette for a Garden Fountain
Group of Nymphs and Satyrs,** 1927
Painted plaster

30 × 12.8 × 10.7cm
Purchased through the HMI Archive
Fund, 1998

1998.0008.0002
**Maquette for a Garden Fountain
Group of Nymphs and Satyrs,** 1927
Painted plaster
32 × 13.3 × 10.5cm
Purchased through the HMI Archive
Fund, 1998

Bruce James b.1939

1972.0001.L
But Drowning, 1972
Perspex and nylon
31 × 27.5 × 25.2cm
Purchased by the LACF, 1972

Samuel Joseph 1791–1850

2005.0491
**Bust of Mrs Susannah Kinnear (née
Gott) (1799–1889),** 1825
Marble
64 × 40 × 28cm
Transferred from Leeds City Museum,
1971

1972.0009
Bust of a Woman, 1827
Marble
65 × 33 × 26cm
Purchased with the aid of a grant from
the Corporation Fund, 1972

Laurence Josephs 1913–1998   A

2000.0006
The Dreamer, 1937
Elm wood
20 × 18 × 15.5cm
Presented by Carole Trelawney, 2000

Anish Kapoor b.1954   D

1994.0057
Void Stone, 1990
Limestone and pigment
125 × 129 × 94cm
Presented by the CAS, 1991

Eric Kennington 1888–1960 A D

2001.0042
Male Baby, *c.*1926
Plaster
19 × 33 × 22.5cm
Presented by Christopher J.
Kennington, 2001

2001.0003.L
Boy on an Engine, 1929
Portland stone
121.5 × 33.5 × 73cm
On permanent loan from the family of
the artist, 2001

1996.0002.L
The War God, 1933–5
Portland stone
135 × 45 × 40cm
On permanent loan from the family of
the artist, 1996

Michael Kenny 1941–1999 D

2005.0010
Tranquil Night, 1980
Resin, plastic and oil paint
25.5 × 244 × 333cm
Presented by the NACF, 2004

Attributed to Auguste van den Kerckhove 1825–1895

2000.0029.T
**Bust of Sir John Savile-Lumley
(1818–1896),** *c.*1868
Marble
68.5 × 48 × 33.5cm
Acquisition source unknown

William Day Keyworth 1817–1897

2005.0506
**Bust of the Rev. Walter Farquhar Hook
(1798–1875),** 1844
Marble
85 × 50 × 41cm
Presented by Mrs Hook, 1859

David Kindersley 1915–1995 after Eric Gill

1990.0001
Garden Roller: Adam and Eve, 1933
Portland stone
130 × 83 × 40cm
Purchased with the aid of grants from
the V&A Purchase Grant Fund, the
NACF, the LACF and the HMF, 1990

Peter King 1928–1957 A

2002.0099
Untitled, 1955
Bronze
14 × 56 × 5.5cm
Purchased through the HMI Archive
Fund, 2002

2002.0098
Untitled, 1955–7
Aluminium
16 × 13 × 2cm
Presented by Katharine King, 2002

Phillip King b.1934

1995.0026
Crouching Man, 1956
Painted clay
17 × 17 × 14cm
Purchased through the HMI Archive
Fund, 1995

1997.0055
Through, 1965
Plastic, fibreglass and MDF
213 × 335 × 274cm
Purchased with the aid of grants from
the HMF and the V&A Purchase Grant
Fund, 1997

Ghisha Koenig 1921–1993   A D

1994.0026
The Paper Counters, 1952
Plaster
44.6 × 58.6 × 3cm
Purchased with the aid of a grant from
the V&A Purchase Grant Fund, 1994

2005.0014
Calendar Shop I, 1970
Bronze
27 × 26.6 × 33cm
Presented by Dr. Emanuel Tuckman,
2002

1994.0027
Glassworks, 1985
Terracotta
59.2 × 44.8 × 6cm
Purchased with the aid of a grant from
the V&A Purchase Grant Fund, 1994

Inman Knox dates unknown

2003.0047
The Twins, 1922
Plaster
19 × 27 × 13cm
Presented by Bernard P. Scattergood,
1922

Bruce Lacey b.1927   A

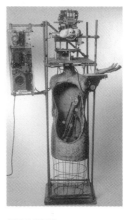

2004.0002
Old Money Bags, 1964
Mixed media
174 × 91 × 49.5cm
Purchased from the artist with the aid
of grants from the NACF and the MLA/
V&A Purchase Grant Fund, 2004

Maurice Lambert 1901–1964

1987.0042
Man and Child, 1931
Verde di Prato marble
94 × 56 × 36cm
Purchased with the aid of grants from
the V&A Purchase Grant Fund and the
HMF, 1987

Langlands & Bell –
Ben Langlands b.1955
and Nikki Bell b.1959   A

2002.0094
First Model for Eclipse, 1998
Card, paper, paint and pencil
15 × 84 × 26cm
Presented by the artists, 1998

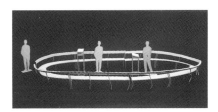

2002.0093
Second Model for Eclipse, 1998
Card, paper, paint and pencil
11 × 53.2 × 38.1 cm
Presented by the artists, 1998

Edouard Lantéri 1848–1917

2004.0014.T
Example of a Study from Life, 1902
Plaster
60 × 49 × 34cm
Purchased 2004

Mervyn Lawrence 1868–1914

1953.0013.0366
The Prodigal Son, 1906
Bronze
65.5 × 54.5 × 47cm
Bequeathed by Agnes and Norman
Lupton, 1953

Gilbert Ledward
1888–1960   A D

2003.0015.T
**Medal for the St. Marylebone
Infirmary, London,** 1915
Bronze
Diam. 4cm
Presented by Mrs Patricia Simon, 2003

2003.0016.T
**Medal for the Institute of Child Health,
London,** 1950
Silver
Diam. 5cm
Presented by Mrs Patricia Simon, 2003

Thomas Stirling Lee 1857–1916

1913.0110.0001
The Music of the Wind, 1907
Silvered bronze
65.5 × 29 × 21cm
Presented through the LACF by Mrs
Sam Wilson, 1925

1913.0110.0002
Maquette for The Music of the Wind,
1907
Wax
72 × 24.5 × 21cm
Presented through the LACF by Mrs
Sam Wilson, 1925

Roger Leigh b.1925

1966.0024.0001
Hydroform, 1965
Wood
89 × 39 × 43cm
Purchased from the artist by the LACF,
1966

Frederic Leighton 1830–1896

1904.0090
The Sluggard, 1890
Bronze
52.8 × 27 × 17cm
Purchased 1904

Liliane Lijn b.1939

1998.0020
Atom Body Was Light, 1963
Letraset and paint on a wooden cone,
with a motorised turntable
40.7 × 11.5 × 17.2cm
Purchased through the HMI Archive
Fund, 1998

Frank Lisle b.1916

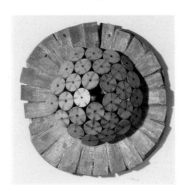

1964.0014
Blue Relief Painting, 1963
Painted wood
Diam. 61cm
Purchased by the LACF, 1964

Richard Long b.1945   D

1996.0053
Untitled (Pot), 1965–6
Painted earthenware and plaster
45.7 × 28 × 28cm

Purchased with the aid of grants from
the V&A Purchase Grant Fund and the
LACF, 1996

1981.0029
Delabole Slate Circle, 1980
Delabole slate
Diam. 480cm
Purchased with the aid of a grant from
the V&A Purchase Grant Fund, 1981

Princess Louise, Duchess of Argyll
1848–1939

1922.0002.T
Queen Victoria (1819–1901), 1887
Bronze
61.5 × 46 × 41cm
Presented by the Earl of Halifax, 1922

Richard Cockle Lucas
1800–1883   A

1927.0716
Bust of a Girl, c.1850
Wax
35 × 31.5 × 11cm
Presented by S. C. Kaines-Smith, 1927

Lucy Lyons 1916–2003

1983.0065.0003
Bust of a Rabbi, 1961
Bronze
51 × 44 × 24cm
Presented by the artist, 1983

1983.0065.0001
Time Remembered, 1975
Bronze
13 × 25 × 14cm
Presented by the artist, 1983

1983.0065.0002
Time Remembered, 1975
Wax
13 × 25 × 14cm
Presented by the artist, 1983

Michael Lyons b.1943   A

1984.0031

Green Bronze IV, 1980
Bronze
16 × 13.5 × 10.5cm
Purchased from the artist with the
aid of a grant from the V&A Purchase
Grant Fund, 1984

Laurence MacDonald 1799–1878

2000.0023.T
Bust of John Marshall (1765–1845),
1828
Marble
62 × 46 × 25cm
Acquisition source unknown

Bezalel Mann b.1917

1964.0019.0001
The Jungle
Olive wood
80 × 79 × 50cm
Presented to the LACF, 1964

Carlo Marochetti 1805–1867 A

2000.0027.T
Bust of the Rev. William Sinclair
(1804–1878), c.1850
Marble
86 × 64 × 40cm
Acquisition source unknown

Mary Martin 1907–1969

1997.0044
Maquette for a Fountain at BP House,
London, 1965
Stainless steel, wood, plastic and paint
53.5 × 53.5 × 16.5cm
Purchased through the HMI Archive
Fund, 1997

Giuseppe Mazza 1653–1741

1945.0018.0001
Madonna and Child, 1720
Limed terracotta and plaster
62 × 53.5 × 8cm
Presented by R.H. Kitson, 1945

Robert Tait McKenzie 1867–1938

1983.0020.0001–0004
Four Masks of Facial Expressions, 1902
Breathlessness
Violent Effort
Fatigue
Exhaustion
Painted plaster
Min. 31.8 × 17 × 13cm
Max. 34.3 × 21 × 15cm
Presented by the Wellcome Institute, 1983

F. E. McWilliam 1909–1992

1987.0039
Bending Figure, 1935
Cherry wood
65 × 12.9 × 16.8cm
Purchased with the aid of a grant from
the V&A Purchase Grant Fund, 1987

1966.0027.0001
Blarney Sword, 1959
Bronze
86 × 13 × 6.5 cm
Presented anonymously to the LACF,
1966

1962.0002
Resistance II, 1961
Bronze
80 × 68 × 47cm
Purchased with the aid of a grant from
the Corporation Fund, 1962

Bernard Meadows
1915–2005   A D

1990.0046
Startled Bird, 1955
Bronze
60.3 × 44 × 29cm
Purchased with the aid of a grant from
the NACF, 1990

Ivan Meštrović 1883–1962   A

1959.0021.0002
**The Reader (Dorothy Una Ratcliffe
1887–1967),** 1919
Bronze
91 × 46 × 70cm
Presented by Mrs Dorothy Una
McGrigor-Phillips, 1959

George Meyrick b.1953   A D

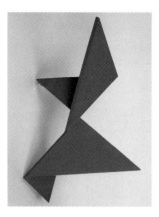

1984.0028
Untitled (Scarlet), 1983
Painted plywood
35.3 × 34.5 × 19.3cm
Purchased from the artist with the
aid of a grant from the V&A Purchase
Grant Fund, 1984

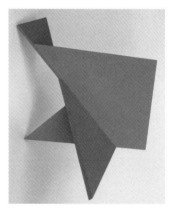

1984.0026
Untitled (Terracotta), 1984
Painted plywood
36 × 43 × 20cm
Purchased from the artist with the
aid of a grant from the V&A Purchase
Grant Fund, 1984

Keith Milow b.1945

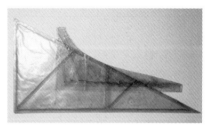

1972.0045.0001
Untitled/Horse, *c.*1972
Fibreglass resin
121.5 × 242 × 5cm
Purchased by the LACF, 1972

Attributed to Raffaelle Monti
1818–1881

1904.0093
Bust of George Canning (1770–1827),
*c.*1850
Marble
71 × 46 × 23cm
Presented by Miss Harding, 1904

Henry Moore 1898–1986   A D

1973.0032.0001
Dancing Figure (Nude Man), 1919–20
Plaster
32.5 × 21 × 2cm
Bequeathed by Jocelyn Horner to the
LACF in memory of Ernest Musgrave,
1973

1973.0033.0001
Seated Nude Man, 1919–20
Plaster

23 × 12 × 17.3cm
Bequeathed by Jocelyn Horner to the
LACF in memory of Ernest Musgrave,
1973

1973.0036.0001
Plate, *c.*1920
Earthenware
Diam. 23.3cm
Bequeathed by Jocelyn Horner to the
LACF in memory of Ernest Musgrave,
1973

1973.0037.0001
Pendant, 1923
Enamel on copper
Diam. 5.8cm
Bequeathed by Jocelyn Horner to the
LACF in memory of Ernest Musgrave,
1973

1946.0020.0001
Maternity, 1924
Hopton Wood stone
20.4 × 14 × 15cm
Presented by the CAS, 1946

1941.0010
Reclining Figure, 1929
Hornton stone
54 × 82 × 37cm
Purchased with the aid of a grant from
the Board of Education, 1941

1983.0047
Mask, 1929
Cast and pigmented concrete, carved
24 × 21 × 12.3cm
Purchased with the aid of grants from
the V&A Purchase Grant Fund and the
HMF, 1983

1999.0029
Mother and Child, 1932
Alabaster
33.5 × 15.5 × 17.5cm
Accepted by HM Government in Lieu
of Inheritance Tax and allocated to
Leeds City Council for display at Leeds
City Art Gallery, 1999

1985.0029
Mother and Child, 1936
Green Hornton stone
162.5 × 41 × 46cm
Presented by the HMF, 1985

1992.0043
Maquette for a Reclining Figure, 1938
Bronze
17 × 32 × 11.5cm
Accepted by HM Government in Lieu
of Inheritance Tax from the estate of
Mrs Ruth Mock in memory of Rudolf
Mock and allocated to Leeds City
Council for display at Leeds City Art
Gallery, 1999

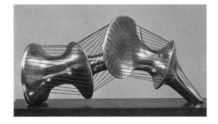

1993.0002.0001
Stringed Figure, 1939
Bronze and thread
29.3 × 14.5 × 11.5cm
Bequeathed by Lady Hendy, 1993

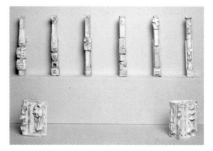

1989.0023.0001–0008
Maquettes for the Sculpture at the
English Electric Company Headquar-
ters on the Strand, London, 1954
Plaster
Dimensions vary: 6 at *c.*30 × 4 × 4cm
and 2 at *c.*15 × 13 × 8cm
Purchased with the aid of grants from
the HMF, the NHMF, the V&A Purchase
Grant Fund, the LACF, the Fabian
Carlsson Gallery, Mrs M. Rosenauer,
Gallery Lingard and an anonymous
benefactor, 1989

1993.0002.0002
Maquette for Upright Motive No.3,
1955
Bronze
25.7 × 7.2 × 6cm
Bequeathed by Lady Hendy, 1993

1993.0002.0002
Maquette for the UNESCO Reclining
Figure, Paris, 1956
Bronze
25.7 × 7.2 × 6cm
Bequeathed by Lady Hendy, 1993

1965.0017.0001
Three-Piece Reclining Figure No.2:
Bridge Prop, 1963
Bronze
251.5 × 112.5 × 132cm
Purchased by the LACF, 1965

1993.0002.0004
Head: Boat Form, *c.*1963
Bronze
15.5 × 8.5 × 9cm
Bequeathed by Lady Hendy, 1993

1993.0002.0005
Maquette for a Three-Piece Sculpture:
Vertebrae, 1968
Bronze
21.5 × 10.5 × 11.5cm
Bequeathed by Lady Hendy, 1993

Anonymous after Henry Moore

1986.0011

Medallion Commemorating the Henry Moore Exhibition *Sculpture, Drawings and Graphics* at the Orangerie, Palais Auersperg, Vienna, 1983
Cupro-nickel
Diam. 3cm
Presented by Steven Gabriel, 1986

Robert Morris b.1931

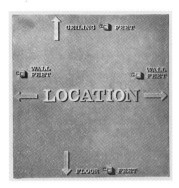

1975.0026
Location, 1973
Lead, aluminium and chipboard
53.7 × 53.5 × 3.5cm
Purchased with the aid of grants from the LACF and the Gulbenkian Foundation, 1975

Attributed to David Morrison
*c.*1793–1850

1983.0033
Portrait of Priscilla Green Bignold, *c.*1825
Coloured wax
14.8 × 7.3 × 3.5 cm
Purchased with the aid of a grant from the Lotherton Hall Endowment Fund, 1983

Marlow Moss 1890–1958

2004.0102.T
Spatial Construction in Steel, 1956–7
Steel
130 × 81.2 × 22.8cm
Purchased with the aid of grants from the NACF, the LACF and the MLA/V&A Purchase Grant Fund, 2004

David Nash b.1945   A D

1994.0049
Pyramid, *c.*1980
Pine wood
35 × 28 × 28cm
Presented by the artist, 1994

1997.0019
Extended Cube, 1996
Cedar wood
94.2 × 98.8 × 275cm
Presented by the artist via the HMF, 1997

Paul Nash 1889–1946

1984.0010
Forest, 1937
Wood
30.5 × 30.5 × 7.5cm
Purchased with the aid of grants from the V&A Purchase Grant Fund and the Paul Nash Trust, 1984

1986.0036
Only Egg, 1937
Photographs, flint and shale
31.9 × 21.2 × 6.7cm
Purchased with the aid of grants from the V&A Purchase Grant Fund and the Paul Nash Trust, 1986

Martin Naylor b.1944   D

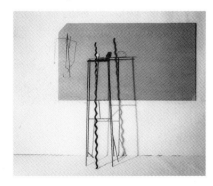

1975.0017
A Young Girl Seated by her Window, 1973
Mixed media
287 × 205.8 × 83.8cm
Purchased with the aid of grants from the V&A Purchase Grant Fund and the LACF, 1975

1995.0018
Important Mischief, 1978
Mixed media
208 × 361 × 216cm
Presented by Jim Moyes of Momart
through the CAS, 1995

Paul Neagu 1938–2004   A D

2003.0038.0001
**Maquette for the Charing Cross Triple
Starhead Commission, London:
Starhead,** c.1986–91
Painted wood
40.5 × 32 × 12.8cm
Purchased from the artist through the
HMI Archive Fund, 2002

2003.0038.0002
**Maquette for the Charing Cross Triple
Starhead Commission, London: Wake,**
c.1986–91
Painted wood
24.6 × 63.5 × 10cm
Purchased from the artist through the
HMI Archive Fund, 2002

E. R. Nele b.1932

2000.0085
Untitled, 1964
Bronze
21 × 11.5 × 1.5cm
Presented by Sara Hicks, 2000

Oscar Nemon 1906–1985   A

2004.0100.T
**Medallion of Charles Lindbergh
(1902–1974),** 1927
Bronze
6.3 × 4 × 0.5cm
Presented by Alice Nemon Stuart, 2004

2004.0101.T
Bust of a Woman, c.1943
Plaster
45 × 34 × 34cm
Presented by Alice Nemon Stuart, 2004

John Newling b.1952

1989.0016
Shelter, 1984
Lead, steel and wax
69 × 35.6 × 50cm
Presented by the CAS, 1989

Uli Nimptsch 1897–1977

1944.0025
Marietta, 1936
Bronze
165 × 50 × 28cm
Purchased with the aid of grants from
the Harding Bequest Fund and the
Corporation Fund, 1944

Matthew Noble 1818–1876

1981.0020
**Bust of Sir Peter Fairbairn (1799–
1861),** 1851
Marble
62 × 56 × 24cm
Purchased 1981

Lucia Nogueira 1950–1998   D

2000.0062
Black, 1994
Fragments of glass chandelier and spotlight
Variable dimensions
Presented by the CAS, 2000

Joseph Nollekens 1737–1823   A

1977.0008
Bust of Lady Louisa Hartley (née Lumley) (1773–1811), 1809
Marble
67.5 × 42 × 22cm
Purchased with the aid of a grant from the V&A Purchase Grant Fund, 1977

Richard Oginz b.1944

1972.0041.L
Ziggurat, 1971 (not illustrated)
Painted wood
101.5 × 274.3 × 274.3cm
Purchased by the LACF, 1972

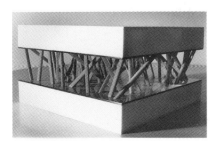

1979.0005
Maquette for Red Sandwich, 1971
Mirror and Perspex
19 × 33 × 33cm

Presented by the Yorkshire Arts Association, 1979

Claes Oldenburg b.1929   D

1981.0015
Soft Drum Set, 1969
Wood, linen and cord, printed with silkscreen
48 × 24.8 × 35cm
Purchased with the aid of a grant from the V&A Purchase Grant Fund, 1981

1992.0060.0001
Maquette for 'A Bottle of Notes', 1990
Wood, paper, plaster, paint and tape
63 × 30.5 × 31cm
Purchased with the aid of a grant from the HMF, 1991

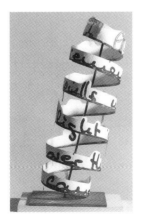

1992.0060.0002
Maquette for 'A Bottle of Notes', 1990
Steel, paper and ink
53 × 22.2 × 27.5cm
Purchased with the aid of a grant from the HMF, 1991

Anders Olson 1880–1955

1925.0212.SW
Girl with a Hoop, c.1904–13
Silvered bronze
38 × 28 × 23cm
Bequeathed by Sam Wilson, 1925

Eduardo Paolozzi
1924–2005   D

1988.0027
Forms on a Bow, 1949
Bronze
63 × 49.5 × 22.5cm
Purchased with the aid of a grant from the HMF, 1988

1988.0044
AG5, 1958
Bronze
103 × 82 × 32cm
Purchased with the aid of a grant from the HMF, 1988

1977.0010
Poem for the Trio M.R.T., 1964
Aluminium
210 × 209 × 112cm
Purchased with the aid of grants from
the Gulbenkian Foundation, the V&A
Purchase Grant Fund and the LACF, 1977

1978.0020
Wittgenstein at Cassino, 1964
Painted aluminium
181.5 × 130.5 × 50.5cm
Purchased with the aid of a grant from
the V&A Purchase Grant Fund, 1978

Edgar George Papworth 1809–1866

2000.0007.T
Bust of a Man, 1856
Marble
74 × 52 × 28cm
Acquisition source unknown

Attributed to Filippo Parodi
1630–1702

1940.0004.0002
Bust of Mars, late 17th century
Marble
70 × 49 × 27cm
Presented by S. Smith, 1940

1940.0004.0003
Bust of Venus, late 17th century
Marble
68 × 49 × 25cm
Presented by S. Smith, 1940

Louise Parsons b.1944

1979.0004
Paint Cupboard, 1973
Wood, metal and perspex
153.2 × 61.7 × 18.8cm
Presented by the Yorkshire Arts
Association, 1978

Victor Pasmore 1908–1998

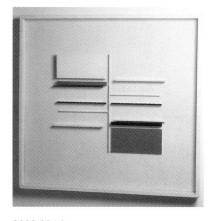

2002.0046
**Abstract in Black, White, Cherry and
Ochre,** 1957
Painted wood
105 × 113.5 × 5cm
Presented by Education Leeds/Artemis
as part of a transfer from the School
Loans Service, 2002

Samuel Percy 1750–1820

1981.0018
Bust of Richard Reynolds (1735–1816),
1810
Coloured wax and wood
37.6 × 33.3 × 12cm (in frame)
Purchased with the aid of a grant from
the V&A Purchase Grant Fund, 1981

Peter (Laszlo) Peri 1899–1967   A

1996.0056
Maquette for a Fountain Sculpture: a Child Astride a Globe, *c.*1930
Concrete and stone
30 × 22.5 × 22.5cm
Purchased with the aid of a grant from the LACF, 1996

1999.0009
Fishing off the Pier, 1937
Coloured concrete
58 × 100.5 × 6cm
Purchased through the HMI Archive Fund, 1999

2000.0066
Bank Holiday, *c.*1937
Coloured concrete
67.2 × 102.4 × 12.8cm
Presented by William Peri, 2000

2000.0071
Little People: a Woman of Authority, 1940s
Coloured concrete
33 × 10.2 × 10.2cm
Presented by William Peri, 2000

2000.0072
Little People: Woman with Folded Arms, 1940s
Coloured concrete
34.3 × 14 × 14cm
Presented by William Peri, 2000

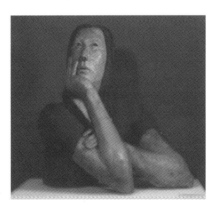

2000.0065
Woman with Red Hair, 1945
Coloured concrete
50.7 × 48.1 × 76cm
Presented by William Peri, 2000

2000.0069
Medallion to Karl Marx (1818–1883), *c.*1945
Coloured concrete
Diam. 22.9cm
Presented by William Peri, 2000

2000.0070
Medallion to the War of 1939–1945, *c.*1945
Coloured concrete
Diam. 22.9cm
Presented by William Peri, 2000

1996.0054
Maquette for a Wall Sculpture: Reclining Woman and Standing Child, *c.*1950
Coloured concrete
57 × 57 × 18cm
Purchased with the aid of a grant from the LACF, 1996

1996.0055
Maquette for a Public Sculpture for a School Playground: Boy and Girl Examining a Flask, *c.*1950
Coloured concrete
18 × 46 × 16cm
Purchased with the aid of a grant from the LACF, 1996

2000.0064
Maquette for the Sculpture at Station Gate on the South Bank, London, for the *Festival of Britain*: the Sunbathers, 1951
Coloured concrete
57 × 45.6 × 16.5cm
Presented by William Peri, 2000

2000.0068
Maquette for a Monument: Woman and Child, mid-1950s
Concrete
71.1 × 33 × 33cm
Presented by William Peri, 2000

2000.0067
Maquette for a Wall Relief at St. Michael's Primary School, Coventry: St. Michael Playing with Children, *c.*1959
Coloured concrete
25.4 × 52.1 × 2.5cm
Presented by William Peri, 2000

Eric Peskett 1917–1997   A D

1999.0021
Gaia, 1994
Wood
15 × 61 × 17cm
Presented by the artist's widow in memory of her husband, 1999

Harry Phillips 1911–1976

1967.0025.0001
Boy, 1954 (cast 1967)
103 × 34 × 21cm
Purchased from the artist with the aid of a grant from the Corporation Fund, 1967

1976.0016.0002
Maquette for a Statue of a Miner at the Richborough Power Station, Kent, 1958

Wax
9.0 × 5.0 × 25.5 cm
Purchased from the artist with the aid of a grant from the Corporation Fund, 1976

1976.0011
Woman Undressing, 1975
Bronze
25.8 × 32.5 × 22.0 cm
Presented by the artist, 1976

1976.0016.0001
Woman with a Chair, *c.*1976
Wax
13.5 × 11.5 × 11.0 cm
Purchased from the artist with the aid of a grant from the Corporation Fund, 1976

Carl Plackman 1943–2004

2005.0494
No Distance Too Short or Too Long,

1973
Photographs and leather on paper in frame
96.5 × 52.8cm
Purchased through the HMI Archive Fund, 2005

2005.0500
Cathedral, 1973
Photograph and ink on paper in frame
96.5 × 52.8cm
Purchased through the HMI Archive Fund, 2005

2005.0499
Containers: The Hardware of Life,
c.1974
Typed paper and flattened tin cans on board in frame
Four parts: 66 × 32cm each
Purchased through the HMI Archive Fund, 2005

Nicholas Pope b.1949

1999.0036
Ten Commandments, 1993
Stoneware fired brick clay
Ten pieces, various heights, between 11.5 and 24cm
Purchased with the aid of a grant from the V&A Purchase Grant Fund and the LACF, 1999

Edward Carter Preston
1885–1965   A

1999.0035
Europa, c.1933
Basalt
35 × 43 × 18.5cm
Purchased with the aid of a grant from the V&A Purchase Grant Fund, 1999

Charles Quick b.1957   A

1985.0012
Maquette for The Tower, 1984
Pine wood and hardboard
22 × 20.5 × 23cm
Presented by the artist, 1985

Peter Randall-Page b.1954   D

1989.0019
Red Fruit, 1987
Red marble on a wooden base
121 × 39 × 39cm
Purchased 1989

Betty Rea 1904–1965   A

2001.0069
Girls in the Wind, 1956–7
Painted plaster
57 × 25 × 19cm
Presented by J.N. and C.J. Rea, 2001

Loris Rey 1903–1962

2002.0090
Bust of Jacob Kramer (1892–1962),
1931
Tinted plaster
50.8 × 25 × 32cm
Presented by Mrs June Rey, 2002

1932.0005
**Cast of the Hands of Berkeley
Moynihan (1865–1936), the First Lord
Moynihan,** 1932
Bronze
21 × 42 × 30cm
Presented by L.R. Braithwaite, 1932

Tessa Robins b.1965

1994.0016.0001
Untitled 92–1, 1992
MDF, birch-ply and Macassar ebony
14.5 × 14.5 × 40cm
Purchased with the aid of grants from
the LACF and the V&A Purchase Grant
Fund, 1994

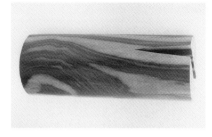

1994.0016.0002
Untitled 92–5, 1992
MDF, birch-ply and Macassar ebony
15.3 × 12.5 × 34.5cm
Purchased with the aid of grants from
the LACF and the V&A Purchase Grant
Fund, 1994

Auguste Rodin 1840–1917   D

1995.0017
Age of Bronze (L'Age d'Airain), 1877
(cast 1906)
Bronze
178 × 60 × 61cm
Purchased with the aid of grants
from the HMF, the NACF, the V&A
Purchase Grant Fund, Raymond and
Mary Danowski, the LACF and various
private benefactors, 1995

1957.0008
**The Large Dancer (La Grande
Danseuse),** c.1911 (cast 1956)

Bronze
69 × 21 × 33cm
Purchased with the aid of grants from
the V&A Purchase Grant Fund and the
Corporation Fund, 1957

Ellen Mary Rope 1855–1934   A

1997.0021
Maquette for a Child's Memorial,
c.1920
Painted plaster
34.5 × 31 × 6.3cm
Purchased by the HMI Archive Fund,
1997

Eva Rothschild b.1972

2002.0089
Bad Hat, 2002
Perspex
239 × 163 × 142cm
Purchased with the aid of grants from
the MLA/V&A Purchase Grant Fund
and LACF, 2002

Louis-Oscar Roty 1846–1911

1899.0410.0001 & 2
Pair of Medallions of Aphrodite and Eros, c.1899
Gilt bronze
Diam. 7.8cm
Purchased 1899

Louis-François Roubiliac 1695–1762

1942.0006
Bust of Alexander Pope (1688–1744), 1738
Marble
36.5 × 27 × 25 cm
Purchased 1942

Matt Rugg b.1935

1963.0016.L
Unit Relief, 1962
Mixed wood
117.2 × 92.5 × 10cm
Purchased by the LACF, 1963

1963.0015.L
Sign Elements III, 1963
Mixed wood
109 × 109 × 10cm
Purchased by the LACF, 1963

Andrew Sabin b.1958

1994.0017
Penn Ponds in Winter, 1989
Cement, plastic, glazed ceramics and steel
34 × 120 × 189cm
Purchased from the artist with the aid of a grant from the V&A Purchase Grant Fund, 1994

Michael Sandle b.1936   A

1991.0006
Belgrano – Medal for Dishonour, 1986
Bronze
Diam. 8.2cm
Presented by the artist, 1991

Francis William Sargant 1870–1960

1958.0014
Lamia, c.1952
Bronze
31 × 15.3 × 15.3cm
Presented anonymously through the LACF, 1958

Peter Scheemakers 1691–1781   D

1986.0013
Maquette for a Figure of Abundance, 1753

Terracotta
49.5 × 18 × 12cm
Purchased with the aid of a grant from
the Brigadier Hargreaves Trust, 1986

Bernard Schottlander
1924–1999   A

2000.0010
Maquette for 3B Series, No.2, 1968
Painted iron
35.5 × 76 × 60.8cm
Presented by Sara Hicks in memory of
Bernard Schottlander, 1999

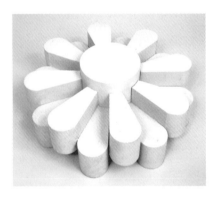

2000.0009
**Maquette for a Public Sculpture at the
Euston Road Housing Estate, London,**
*c.*1970
Painted aluminium
55 × 55 × 22cm
Presented by Sara Hicks in memory of
Bernard Schottlander, 1999

2000.0008
Maquette for South of the River, 1976
Aluminium
23 × 48 × 29cm
Presented by Sara Hicks in memory of
Bernard Schottlander, 1999

Julian Schwarz   b.1949   D

1980.0015
Screen, 1977
Sycamore wood
78 × 49.5 × 7.4cm
Purchased with the aid of a grant from
the Corporation Fund, 1980

Kathleen Scott   1878–1947

1949.0004.0002
**Statuette of Charles Shannon (1865–
1937),** *c.*1910
Bronze
34.5 × 13 × 27.5cm
Presented by the Rt. Hon. Lord Kennet,
1949

1949.0004.0003
**Statuette of Charles De Soussy Ricketts
(1866–1931),** *c.*1910

Bronze
34.5 × 13 × 27.5cm
Presented by the Rt. Hon. Lord Kennet,
1949

1949.0004.0001
Bust of John Galsworthy (1867–1933),
*c.*1920
Bronze
34 × 21 × 20cm
Presented by the Rt. Hon. Lord Kennet,
1949

Harry Seager   b.1931

1965.0013
Chopper and Changer, 1965
Glass
146 × 50 × 27cm
Purchased with the aid of a grant from
the Calouste Gulbenkian Foundation,
1965

Ernest Sichel 1862–1941

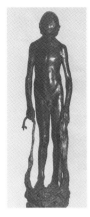

1901.0092
The Sea Star, *c.*1900
Bronze
47 × 11.5 × 13.5cm
Purchased 1901

Edward Caldwell Spruce
*c.*1866–1922

1925.0337.SW
Bust of Sam Wilson (1857–1918), 1897
Bronze
69 × 46.5 × 28.5cm
Bequeathed by Sam Wilson, 1925

1907.0098
The Day is Dark and the Night, *c.*1907
Bronze
56 × 28 × 27cm
Purchased with the aid of a grant from
the Corporation Fund, 1907

1907.0104
**Bust of Sir James Kitson, Lord Airedale
(1835–1911),** *c.*1907
Marble
66.5 × 62.5 × 33cm
Purchased 1907

2003.0045
**Life Study: Nude Man Holding his
Foot,** 1910
Painted plaster
89 × 33 × 32cm
Purchased 1910

1917.0267
Medallion of Phil May (1864–1903),
1917
Bronze
Diam. 26.8 cm
Purchased by public subscription, 1917

Peter Startup 1921–1976

2001.0088
Reflection, 1967
Painted wood
130.8 × 75.7 × 75.7cm
Presented by the Royal Academy of Arts
(Chantrey Bequest), 2001

John Macallan Swan 1847–1910

1925.0213.SW
Bear's Head, *c.*1900
Bronze
10.5 × 9.5 × 12.2cm
Bequeathed by Sam Wilson, 1925

William Theed 1804–1891

1967.0024.0040
Narcissus, *c.*1848
Marble
117 × 60 × 39.5cm
Bequeathed by Mrs Dorothy Una
McGrigor-Phillips, 1967

Leslie Thornton b.1925

1958.0011.0001
The Gladiators, *c.*1958
Bronze, copper and brass
79 × 48 × 35cm
Purchased from the artist by the LACF,
1958

Mary Thornycroft (née Francis)
1809–1895 A

1997.0001
**Bust of Viscountess Mahon (1815–
1873)**, 1852
Marble
58 × 49 × 32cm
Purchased through the HMI Archive
Fund, 1997

2001.0065
Bust of a Grecian Woman, undated

Marble
29.5 × 15.5 × 20cm
Bequeathed by Gervase Farjeon, 2001

William Hamo Thornycroft
1850–1925 A D

1987.0024.0001
Tidnock Farm, Cheshire, 1861
Plaster
8.5 × 13.7 × 3cm
Bequeathed by Mrs Elfrida Manning,
1987

1987.0024.0002
Artemis and Her Hound, 1880
Bronzed plaster
106 × 40 × 4cm
Bequeathed by Mrs Elfrida Manning,
1987

1987.0024.0003
Maquette for Teucer, *c.*1881
Tinted plaster
21.5 × 14.5 × 3cm
Bequeathed by Mrs Elfrida Manning,
1987

1983.0063
Maquette for The Mower, *c.*1884
Wax
23.5 × 11.5 × 11.5cm
Presented by Mrs Elfrida Manning,
1983

1984.0022
**Statuette of General Charles Gordon
for The Embankment, London
(1833–1885)**, 1888
Bronze
38 × 11.5 × 10cm
Purchased with the aid of a grant from
the V&A Purchase Grant Fund, 1984

1988.0020
Maquette for The Mirror, 1889
Plaster
78 × 68 × 4cm
Purchased with the aid of a grant from
the V&A Purchase Grant Fund, 1988

2003.0100.0015.T
Maquette for an Equestrian Statue of Edward I (1239–1307), *c.*1893
Plasticine
15 × 8.5 × 15cm
Transferred from the University of Reading, 2003

2003.0100.0001.T
Maquette for a Statuette of a Woman Washing, 1895
Plaster and shellac
17 × 11 × 12cm
Transferred from the University of Reading, 2003

1987.0024.0006
Joy of Life, 1896
Bronze
39 × 23 × 12cm
Bequeathed by Mrs Elfrida Manning, 1987

1987.0024.0007
The Bather, 1898
Painted plaster
56.5 × 15.5 × 13.5cm
Bequeathed by Mrs Elfrida Manning, 1987

2001.0064
Cast of the Hand of Joan Thornycroft (b.1888), 1899
Plaster
7.5 × 20.5 × 14cm
Bequeathed by Gervase Farjeon, 2001

1987.0024.0008
Bust of Agatha Thornycroft (1864–1958), 1900
Plaster
18.5 × 8.5 × 11.8cm
Bequeathed by Mrs Elfrida Manning, 1987

2001.0058
Medallion Portrait of Agatha Thornycroft (1864–1958), *c.*1900
Wax
Diam. 7.6 cm
Bequeathed by Mrs Elfrida Manning, 1987

2003.0100.0011.T
Maquette for the Monument to John Colet (1467–1519), Dean of St. Paul's, London, 1900
Plasticine
18 × 13 × 11cm
Transferred from the University of Reading, 2003

2003.0100.0014.T
Maquette for the Statue of Alfred the Great (849–899), Winchester, *c.*1901
Painted plaster
37.5 × 13 × 12cm
Transferred from the University of Reading, 2003

2003.0100.0002.T
Maquette for the Statue of William Ewart Gladstone (1809–1898) on The Strand, London, *c.*1905
Plaster
24.1 × 23.5 × 12cm
Transferred from the University of Reading, 2003

2003.0100.0003.T
Maquette for the Statue of William Ewart Gladstone (1809–1898) on The Strand, London, *c.*1905
Plaster
39 × 17 × 15cm
Transferred from the University of Reading, 2003

2003.0100.0010.T
Maquette for the Figure of Courage on the Gladstone Memorial on The Strand, London, *c.*1905

Plasticine
23 × 7.5 × 9.2cm
Transferred from the University of Reading, 2003

2003.0100.0021.T
Maquette for William Conyngham (1828–1897), 4ᵗʰ Baron Plunket, Archbishop of Dublin, Kildare Place, Dublin, *c.*1905
Plaster
26.5 × 10 × 10.2cm
Transferred from the University of Reading, 2003

1987.0024.0009
Bust of Elfrida Thornycroft (b.1901), 1909
Plaster
39.5 × 23 × 20cm
Bequeathed by Mrs Elfrida Manning, 1987

2003.0100.0012.T
Maquette for the Statue of Alfred, Lord Tennyson (1809–1892) at Trinity College, Cambridge, *c.*1909
Plasticine
14.5 × 7 × 7cm
Transferred from the University of Reading, 2003

2003.0100.0018.T
Maquette for Alfred, Lord Tennyson seated (1809–1892) at Trinity College, Cambridge, *c.*1909
Plaster
21 × 12.8 × 17
Transferred from the University of Reading, 2003

2003.0100.0009.T
Maquette for The Kiss, *c.*1916
Painted plaster
34.2 × 11 × 13cm

Transferred from the University of Reading, 2003

2001.0063
Morning, 1919
Bronze
27 × 9.3 × 7.5cm
Bequeathed by Gervase Farjeon, 2001

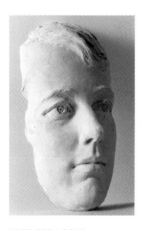

1987.0024.0010
Face Mask of Elfrida Thornycroft, 1923
Unfired clay
21.5 × 12 × 6.5cm
Bequeathed by Mrs Elfrida Manning, 1987

1987.0024.0011
Self-Portrait Bust, 1923
Plaster
20 × 12 × 11.5cm
Bequeathed by Mrs Elfrida Manning, 1987

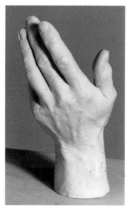

1987.0024.0012
Cast of a Hand, 1923
Plaster
23 × 16 × 9.5cm
Bequeathed by Mrs Elfrida Manning, 1987

1987.0024.0013
Maquette for a Statuette of a Farm Hand Carrying a Calf, 1925
Plaster
30.6 × 15 × 11cm
Bequeathed by Mrs Elfrida Manning, 1987

2001.0060
Corky, undated
Bronze
18 × 27.8 × 12.5cm
Bequeathed by Gervase Farjeon, 2001

2001.0062
Cherub on a Wine Cask, undated
Painted plaster
20.4 × 11 × 9.5cm
Bequeathed by Gervase Farjeon, 2001

2001.0066–67
Material from the studio of William Hamo Thornycroft including casts from the antique, undated
Bequeathed by Gervase Farjeon, 2001

2003.0100.0004.T
Maquette for the Figure of a Girl Running, undated
Plaster
17.1 × 8.5 × 8.5cm
Transferred from the University of Reading, 2003

2003.0100.0005.T
Maquette for a Monumental Plinth,
undated
Plaster and plasticine
22.5 × 15 × 16.2cm
Transferred from the University of
Reading, 2003

2003.0100.0013.T
Maquette for a Figure of Justice,
undated
Plaster
24.2 × 9.7 × 6.5
Transferred from the University of
Reading, 2003

2003.0100.0019.T
**Maquette for Joshua Reynolds seated
with Child,** undated
Plasticine
19.5 × 11 × 9cm
Transferred from the University of
Reading, 2003

2003.0100.0006.T
Maquette for the Figure of an Orator,
undated
Plasticine
20.5 × 14.7 × 7.5cm
Transferred from the University of
Reading, 2003

2003.0100.0016.T
Maquette for a Figure of Grief, undated
Plasticine
20 × 8 × 11.5cm
Transferred from the University of
Reading, 2003

2003.0100.0020.T
**Maquette for the Figure of a Woman
Golfer,** undated
Plasticine
23 × 9.5 × 13cm
Transferred from the University of
Reading, 2003

2003.0100.0007.T
**Maquette for the Figures of a Mother
and Child,** undated
Plasticine
21.5 × 8 × 12.6cm
Transferred from the University of
Reading, 2003

2003.0100.0017.T
**Maquette for a Figure of a Washer-
Woman,** undated
Plasticine
14.5 × 9.5 × 9cm
Transferred from the University of
Reading, 2003

Berthel Thorvaldsen 1770–1843

1904.0001
The Virgin and Child with St. John, 1806
Plaster
68 × 61 × 6.5cm
Presented by Miss S.J. Harding, 1904

John Throp 1819–1889

2000.0030.T
Bust of Obadiah Nussey (c.1837–1901), 1876
Marble
73.5 × 59 × 33cm
Purchased c.1906

Harry Thubron 1915–1985

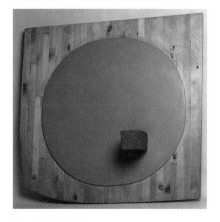

1964.0006.0001
Red Circle, 1964

Painted pine wood
73.2 × 72 × 20cm
Purchased by the LACF, 1964

1985.0021
Uomo, 1985
Mixed media
74 × 61.2 × 6.5cm
Purchased with the aid of grants from the V&A Purchase Grant Fund and the LACF, 1985

Albert Toft 1862–1949   A

2000.0012
Maquette for Hagar, c.1899
Plaster
23 × 11 × 17cm
Presented by Phillip Richardson, 2000

2000.0015
Maquette for Hagar, c.1899
Tinted plaster
23 × 11 × 17cm
Presented by Phillip Richardson, 2000

2002.0102
Self-Portrait Bust, c.1900

Painted plaster
24 × 16.5 × 11.5cm
Purchased through the HMI Archive Fund, 2002

2000.0014
Maquette for The Metal Pourer, c.1913
Painted plaster
33 × 22 × 17cm
Presented by Phillip Richardson, 2000

2000.0011
Maquette for Joie de Vivre, 1927
Plaster
22 × 9.5 × 5cm
Presented by Phillip Richardson, 2000

2000.0013
Maquette for Joie de Vivre, 1927
Tinted plaster
22 × 9.5 × 5cm
Presented by Phillip Richardson, 2000

2003.0024
Medallion of Ellen Terry (1848–1928),
1936
Tinted plaster
Diam. 18cm
Presented by Nina Troitzky-Richardson,
2002

David Tremlett b.1945

2001.0026.0001–0002
Postcard Work, 1971
Postcards and paper
2 pieces, each 53.5 × 104.7 × 3cm
Purchased from the artist through the
HMI Archive Fund, 2001

William Tucker b.1935

1969.0031.0001
Series A No.II, 1968
Fibreglass
83 × 228.6 × 210.8cm
Purchased by the LACF, 1969

1997.0057
Maquette for a Large-Scale Sculpture,
1994
Plaster
19.3 × 19 × 15cm
Presented by the artist, 1996

William Turnbull b.1922

2002.0042
Playground (Game), 1949 (cast 2002)
Bronze
11.4 × 48.3 × 70cm
Purchased from the artist with the aid
of a grant from the MLA/V&A Purchase
Grant Fund, 2002

Peter Turnerelli 1774–1839

1971.0033
Bust of Queen Charlotte (1744–1818),
1818
Marble
44.5 × 29 × 19cm
Purchased 1971

Gunther Uecker b.1930

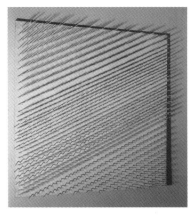

1966.0025.0001
Diagonal Structure, 1966
Painted blockboard and nails
102 × 102 × 8cm
Presented anonymously to the LACF,
1966

Leon Underwood
1890–1975 A D

1995.0028
Family, c.1935
Rosewood
70 × 40 × 32cm
Purchased with the aid of a grant from
the HMF, 1995

Paule Vézelay 1892–1984 A

1994.0032
Dish with a Little Boat, 1936
Plaster
22 × 7.5 × 15cm
Purchased through the HMI Archive
Fund, 1994

Auke de Vries b.1937   A

1996.0036
**Maquette for a Sculpture at the Chris-
telijke Hogeschool, Leeuwarden,** 1993
Steel and iron
66.8 × 23 × 18cm
Presented by the artist, 1996

Henry Weekes 1807–1877

1972.0005
**Bust of Hugh Richard Fahie Hoare
(1827–1840),** 1840
Marble
61 × 39 × 27cm
Purchased with the aid of funds from
the Oxley Bequest, 1972

1904.0085
The Young Naturalist, 1870
Marble
145 × 57 × 57cm
Presented by Miss S. J. Harding, 1904

Charles Wheeler 1892–1974   A

2002.0100
**Bust of Carol Rosemary Wheeler
(b.1927),** 1927
Gilt bronze
16.8 × 9.2 × 12.3cm
Purchased through the HMI Archive
Fund, 2002

2002.0101
**Model of the Springbok at South Africa
House, Trafalgar Square, London,**
*c.*1935
Gilt bronze and onyx
35.7 × 6.7 × 14.8cm
Purchased through the HMI Archive
Fund, 2002

Frederick John Wilcoxson
1888–*c.*1939

2003.0016

**Bust of Henry Cawood Embleton
(*fl.*1897–1930),** 1924
Marble
56 × 27.5 × 28cm
Presented by the Leeds Choral Union,
1924

Alison Wilding b.1948   D

1996.0060
Temper, 1991–2
Perspex, steel, rubber and glass
263 × 204 × 61cm
Purchased with the aid of grants from
the V&A Purchase Grant Fund and the
LACF, 1996

2005.0013
Cold Face, 1997
Stainless steel, cast silicone rubber and
wood
14 × 352.5 × 127cm
Gift of an anonymous donor, presented
through the CAS and the HMF, 2003

Stephen Willats b.1943   A D

1989.0005
The Doppelgänger, 1984
Mixed media on board
Each 136 × 206 × 4cm
Purchased with the aid of a grant from
the LACF, 1989

Gerard Williams b.1959

2000.0081
Held, 1988
Nylon fabric in an oak frame
48.3 × 48.3 × 7.6cm
Presented by the CAS, 2000

Glynn Williams b.1939

1988.0045
Small Stone Bridge, 1988
Hopton Wood stone
15 × 11.7 × 45cm
Purchased 1988

Keith Wilson b.1965

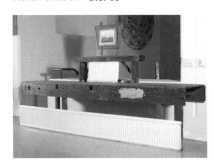

2000.0083
Scape, 1995
Mixed media
196 × 372 × 79cm
Presented by Charles Saatchi via the
NACF, 2000

Gillian Wise b.1936

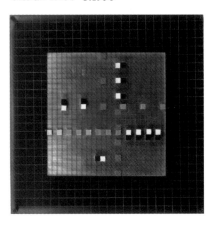

2002.0034
Maquette for XRL2, 1986
Perspex, chipboard and aluminium
60.8 × 60.8 × 11.5cm
Purchased from the artist through the
HMI Archive Fund, 2002

Francis Derwent Wood
1871–1926   D

1925.0214.SW
Bacchante, *c.*1907
Bronze
46 × 14 × 15cm
Bequeathed by Sam Wilson, 1925

Bill Woodrow b.1948   A D

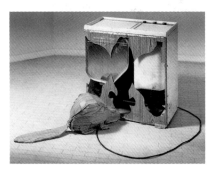

1988.0026
Twin-Tub with Beaver, 1981
Mixed media
78.5 × 73 × 41cm
Presented by the CAS, 1986

Malcolm Woodward b.1943

1983.0067.0001–2
Seated Woman and Seated Man, 1982
Plaster
22.2 × 15 × 15cm and 20.9 × 16 × 17.5cm
Presented by the artist, 1983

1984.0015.0001–2

Girl on a Stool and Youth on a Chair, 1982
Bronze
12.3 × 5 × 7cm and 13 × 7.5 × 6.5cm
Purchased with the aid of a grant from V&A Purchase Grant Fund, 1984

Thomas Woolner 1825–1892   A

2000.0020.T
Bust of John Fowler (1826–1864), 1866
Marble
66 × 2 × 26cm
Acquisition source unknown

1972.0037.0006
Bust of William Hey (1796–1875), 1868
Marble
70 × 38 × 22cm
Presented by United Leeds Hospitals, 1972

Austin Wright 1911–1997   A D

1958.0002.0001
Emerging Form, 1942
Yew wood
46.5 × 19 × 14cm
Presented by Frank Lambert in memory of his wife, 1958

1950.0031
Female Figure, 1944
Yew wood
67.5 × 40 × 34cm
Purchased 1950

1991.0034.0005
Hammerhead, 1956
Lead
31 × 15 × 9.5cm
Bequeathed by R. L. Holmes, 1991

1962.0024
Moon, 1962
Aluminium
320 × 42 × 69cm
Purchased from the artist with the aid of a grant from the Corporation Fund, 1962

1967.0003.L
Relief Model of the Façade of Leeds City Art Gallery, 1967
Wood and aluminium
65.5 × 170.2 × 3.5cm
Gift of Arts Council England, 2006

1967.0004.0002
Maquette for Section No.5 of a Frieze for the Façade of Leeds City Art Gallery, 1967
Aluminium and wood
60.5 × 63 × 5cm
Gift of Arts Council England, 2006

Richard James Wyatt
1795–1850   D

1967.0024.0041
Nymph Removing a Thorn from a Greyhound's Foot, 1848
Marble
193 × 69.5 × 69.5cm
Bequeathed by Mrs Dorothy Una McGrigor-Phillips, 1967

1981.0019
Bust of a Woman, undated
Marble
60.5 × 24 × 41cm
Purchased with the aid of a grant from the V&A Purchase Grant Fund, 1981

Edward William Wyon   1811–1885

1982.0045.0003
Medallion to Francis Chantrey (1781–1841), 1846
Bronze
Diam. 5.5cm
Presented by Jacob Simon, 1982

Harold J. Youngman   1887–c.1973

24.14/87
General Gordon (after W. H. Thornycroft), 1938
Plaster
24 × 8 × 6.5cm
Bequeathed by Mrs Elfrida Manning, 1987

Chronological list of works

16th century	Head of a Man, Anonymous
1684	Charles II on Horseback by Jean Cavalier
17th century	Bust of Septimus Severus, Anonymous
17th century	Bust of Caligula, Anonymous
17th century	Bust of Claudius, Anonymous
17th century	Bust of Marcus Brutus, Anonymous
17th century	Bust of Nero, Anonymous
17th century	Bust of Lucius Verius, Anonymous
17th century	Bust of Vitellius, Anonymous
late 17th century	Lion Attacking a Horse, (Attrib to) Caspar Gras
late 17th century	Bust of Mars (Attrib to) Filippo Parodi
late 17th century	Bust of Venus (Attrib to) Filippo Parodi
early 18th century	Pair of Putti, Anonymous
1704	Bust of a Boy by Jan Claudius De Cock
1712	Statue of Anne I by Andrew Carpenter
1720	Madonna and Child by Giuseppe Mazza
1738	Bust of Alexander Pope by Louis Francois Roubiliac
1753	Maquette for a Figure of Abundance by Peter Scheemakers
c.1754	Bust of Marcus Tullius Cicero by John Cheere
c.1754	Bust of Lucius Annaeus Seneca by John Cheere
c.1754	Bust of Quintus Horatius Flaccus [Horace] by John Cheere
1775–9	Alcyone Discovering the Body of Ceyx by Thomas Banks
1778	Bust of Sir Thomas Gascoigne (Attrib to) Christopher Hewetson
1779	Bust of Mrs Martha Swinburne (Attrib to) Christopher Hewetson
1779	Bust of Henry Swinburne (Attrib to) Christopher Hewetson
19th century	Mercury, Anonymous after Giambologna
19th century	Bust of a Woman with braided hair, Anonymous
19th century	Maquette for a Seated Man in Classical Dress, Anonymous
1801	Portrait of Henry Blundell by George Bullock
1806	The Virgin and Child with St. John by Berthel Thorvaldsen
1809	Bust of Lady Louisa Hartley by Joseph Nollekens
1810	Bust of Richard Reynolds by Samuel Percy
c.1816	Charity by John Flaxman
1816	Bust of William Hey by George Bullock
1817–20	Venus by Antonio Canova

1818	Bust of Queen Charlotte by Peter Turnerelli
1824	Venus Dissuading Adonis from the Chase by Joseph Gott
1824	The Penitent Magdalene by Joseph Gott
c.1885	Portrait of Priscilla Green Bignold (Attrib to) David Morrison
1825	Three Nymphs Carrying Cupid in Triumph by Joseph Gott
1825	Bust of Mrs Susannah Kinnear by Samuel Joseph
1827	Maquette for A Pastoral Apollo by Joseph Gott
1827	Greyhound by Joseph Gott
1827	Bust of a Woman by Samuel Joseph
1828	Bust of Elizabeth Goodman Banks by Joseph Gott
1828	Bust of Eros by Joseph Gott
1828	Bust of George Banks by Joseph Gott
1828	George Banks Seated by Joseph Gott
1828	Maquette for Greek Boxer Awaiting his Turn by Joseph Gott
1828	Maquette for George Banks Seated by Joseph Gott
1828	Maquette for Elizabeth Goodman Banks Seated by Joseph Gott
1828	Bust of Elizabeth Goodman Banks by Joseph Gott
1828	Bust of Benjamin Gott by Joseph Gott
1828	Bust of John Marshall by Laurence MacDonald
1829	Bust of a Satyr by Joseph Gott
1829	Maquette for Margaret Gott as a Babe in the Wood by Joseph Gott
1829	Maquette for Jane Gott as a Babe in the Wood by Joseph Gott
1830	Medallion Portrait of Jean-Pierre Beranger by Pierre Jean David D'Angers
1830	Metobus and Camilla by Joseph Gott
1830s	Bust of Napoleon I by Joseph Gott after Canova
1834	Medallion Portrait of Mrs Elizabeth Allan by Joseph Gott
1834	Greyhound by Joseph Gott
1834	Medallion Portrait of Mrs Mary Brooke by Joseph Gott
1834–5	Bust of John Gott by Joseph Gott
1834–5	Bust of William Gott by Joseph Gott
1835	Medallion Portrait of Mrs Elizabeth Gott by Joseph Gott
1835	Medallion Portrait of Mrs Margaret Gott by Joseph Gott
1835	Medallion Portrait of Benjamin Gott by Joseph Gott

1835	Cupid and Psyche by Joseph Gott
1836	Bust of Michael Sadler (marble) by William Behnes
1836	Bust of Michael Sadler (plaster) by William Behnes
1836	Bust of William Hey by William Behnes
1836	Medallion Portrait of Harriet Gott by Joseph Gott
c.1840	Bust of Benjamin Disraeli, Anonymous
1840	Bust of Hugh Richard Fahie Hoare by Henry Weekes
1844	Bust of the Rev. Walter Farquhar Hook by William Day Keyworth
1846	Medallion to Francis Chantrey by Edward William Wyon
c.1848	Narcissus by William Theed
1848	Nymph Removing a Thorn from a Greyhound's Foot by Richard James Wyatt
undated	Bust of a Woman by Richard James Wyatt
mid-19th century	Princess Marie Pauline Borghese as Venus Victrix, Anonymous, after Canova
mid-19th century	The Wounded Philoctetes, Anonymous after Louis-Marie-Charles-Henri Dupaty
c.1850	Bust of a Girl by Richard Cockle Lucas
c.1850	Bust of George Canning (Attrib to) Raffaelle Monti
c.1850	Bust of the Rev. William Sinclair by Carlo Marochetti
undated	Bust of a Grecian Woman by Mary Thornycroft
1851	Bust of Sir Peter Fairbairn by Matthew Noble
1852	Bust of Viscountess Mahon by Mary Thornycroft
1856	Bust of a Man by Edgar George Papworth
1858	Statue of Victoria I by Matthew Noble
c.1865	Bust of Alderman Kitson by Alfred Bromley
1865	Bust of William Ewart Gott by John Adams-Acton
1865	Statue of Albert, the Prince Consort by Matthew Noble
1866	Bust of John Fowler by Thomas Woolner
1868	Bust of Edward, the Prince of Wales by Matthew Noble
1868	Bust of Alexandra, the Princess of Wales by Matthew Noble
1868	Bust of William Hey by Thomas Woolner
1857	Bust of Richard Hobson by Alfred Bromley
1867	Bust of Thomas Pridgin Teale by Thomas Earle
1870	The Young Naturalist by Henry Weekes
1872	Roundel Portrait of Francis William Green by Joseph Edward Boehm
1872	Roundel Portrait of Edward Lycett Green by Joseph Edward Boehm
1877 (cast 1906)	Age of Bronze (L'Age d'Airain) by Auguste Rodin
1879	Mother and Child by Edward Onslow Ford
1882	Bust of John Deakin Heaton by Henry Hugh Armstead
1883	Perseus Arming by Alfred Gilbert
c.1884	Maquette for the Head of Icarus by Alfred Gilbert
c.1886	Bust of John Barran by John Adams Acton
1887	La Charmeuse [The Snake Charmer] by Michel Leonard Beguine
1887	La Liseuse [The Reader] by Albert-Ernest Carrier-Belleuse
1887	Queen Victoria by Princess Louise
1889–93	St. Christina by George Frampton
1890	The Sluggard by Frederick Leighton
1893	Circe by Alfred Drury
c.1897	Maquette for the Sir William Lawrence Gold Annual Award Medal by Alfred Gilbert
1897	Bust of Victoria I, Anonymous
c.1900	Bust of Mrs Beckett, Anonymous
late 19th century	Bust of James Watt, Anonymous after Francis Legatt Chantrey
late 19th century	Bust of Christina Rossetti, Anonymous
1897	Bust of Sam Wilson by Edward Caldwell Spruce
1897–9	La Chanteuse [The Singer] by Alexandre Louis Marie Charpentier
1897–9	La Fille au Violin [Girl Playing the Violin] by Alexandre Louis Marie Charpentier
c.1899	Medallion of Aphrodite and Eros (x2) by Louis-Oscar Roty
c.1899	Maquette for Hagar (plaster) by Albert Toft
c.1899	Maquette for Hagar (tinted plaster) by Albert Toft
c.1900	The Sea Star by Ernest Sichel
c.1900	Bear's Head by John Macallan Swan
c.1900	Self-Portrait Bust by Albert Toft
c.1900	Bacchante by Francis Derwent Wood
1900	Bust of Cardinal Henry Edward Manning by John Adams-Acton
1900	The Veiled Venus by Kuhne Beveridge and Ella von Wrede
1902	Bust of Sir Douglas Galton by Thomas Brock
1902	Example of a Study from Life by Edouard Lanteri
1902	Four Masks of Facial Expressions by Robert Tait McKenzie
c.1904–13	Girl with a Hoop by Anders Olson

1904	Baby Asleep (x3) by Jacob Epstein
1905	The Little Sea Maiden by Frances Darlington
1906	The Prodigal Son by Mervyn Lawrence
1906	Bust of James Keir Hardie, Anonymous
c.1907	The Day is Dark and the Night by Edward Caldwell Spruce
c.1907	Bust of Sir James Kitson, Lord Airedale by Edward Caldwell Spruce
1907	The Music of the Wind by Thomas Stirling Lee
1907	Maquette for The Music of the Wind by Thomas Stirling Lee
undated	Maquette for the Stamp of the O.W. Paper Art Company Ltd by Alfred Gilbert
undated	Maquette for an Octagonal Plaque by Alfred Gilbert
undated	Maquette for a Panel with a Seated Figure by Alfred Gilbert
undated	Maquette for a Key Bow with a Cupid Whispering to a Seated Girl: Sketch for the Central Group by Alfred Gilbert
undated	Maquette for a Key Bow with a Cupid Whispering to a Seated Girl: with Central Group Detached in the Round by Alfred Gilbert
undated	Maquette for a Key Bow with a Cupid Whispering to a Seated Girl: Central Group with a Frame of Scrolls by Alfred Gilbert
undated	Maquette for a Key Bow (or Finial) with an Allegory of Love by Alfred Gilbert
undated	Maquette for a Pendant with the Dead Christ Sustained by Two Angels by Alfred Gilbert
undated	Maquette for a Pendant with an Arabesque Escutcheon by Alfred Gilbert
undated	Maquette for a Pendant with Two Figures Hanging Over the Figure of a Child by Alfred Gilbert
c.1908–14	The Sam Wilson Chimneypiece by Alfred Gilbert
c.1908–14	Maquette for the Sam Wilson Chimneypiece (x8) by Alfred Gilbert
c.1908–14	Maquette for the Sam Wilson Chimneypiece: Cockerel on a Skull by Alfred Gilbert
1910	Bust of Mary McEvoy by Jacob Epstein
1910	Maternity by Jacob Epstein
1910	Mother and Child by Eric Gill
1910	Life Study: Nude Man Holding his Foot by Edward Caldwell Spruce
c.1910	Statuette of Charles Shannon by Kathleen Scott
c.1910	Statuette of Charles De Soussy Ricketts by Kathleen Scott
c.1910s	Architectural Panel: Beach Scene (Attrib. to) Hermon Cawthra
c.1911 (cast 1956)	The Large Dancer (La Grande Danseuse) by Auguste Rodin
c.1911	Nan Condron by Jacob Epstein
1911	Bust of Lady Isobella Augusta Gregory by Jacob Epstein
1911	Bust of Marie Rankin by Jacob Epstein
1912	The Wrestler by Henri Gaudier-Brzeska
1912–13	Odalisque (Man and Woman) by Henri Gaudier-Brzeska
c.1913	Maquette for The Metal Pourer by Albert Toft
1913	Medallion Portrait of Mary Theresa Odell by Isaac Cooke
1913	Bust of Horace Brodzky by Henri Gaudier-Brzeska
1915	Medal for the St. Marylebone Infirmary, London by Gilbert Ledward
1917	Medallion of Phil May by Edward Caldwell Spruce
1919	The Reader (Dorothy Una Ratcliffe) by Ivan Meštrović
1919–20	Dancing Figure (Nude Man) by Henry Moore
1919–20	Seated Nude Man by Henry Moore
c.1920	Owl by Harold Dow
c.1920	Maquette for a Child's Memorial by Ellen Mary Rope
c.1920	Bust of John Galsworthy by Kathleen Scott
c.1920	Plate by Henry Moore
1921	Bust of Jacob Kramer by Jacob Epstein
1921	Peggy Jean Laughing by Jacob Epstein
1922	Head of Victory from the Leeds War Memorial by Henry Charles Fehr
1922	Bust of Thomas Ashby by Alfred Hardiman
1922	The Twins by Inman Knox
1923	Pendant by Henry Moore
1924	Bust of a Man by P.M.B Blundell
1924	Bust of Henry Cawood Embleton by Frederick John Wilcoxson
1924	Maternity by Henry Moore
c.1926	Male Baby by Eric Kennington
c.1926–7	Bust of Winifred Monnington by Alfred Horace Gerrard
1927	Maquette for Two Greyhounds by William Reid Dick
1927	Maquette for a Garden Fountain Group of Nymphs and Satyrs (x2) by Charles Sargeant Jagger
1927	Maquette for Joie de Vivre (plaster) by Albert Toft

1927	Maquette for Joie de Vivre (tinted plaster) by Albert Toft
1927	Bust of Carol Rosemary Wheeler by Charles Wheeler
c.1928	Maquettes for The North Wind (possibly for that at St. James' Park Underground Station, 55 Broadway, London) (x3) by Alfred Horace Gerrard
1928	Peggy Jean (Sick Child) by Jacob Epstein
1928	Bust of John Galsworthy by David Evans
1929	Boy on an Engine by Eric Kennington
1929	Reclining Figure by Henry Moore
1929	Mask by Henry Moore
c.1930	Maquette for a Fountain Sculpture: a Child Astride a Globe by Peter (Laszlo)Peri
1930	Construction in Space: Soaring by Naum Gabo
1930	Torso by Barry Hart
1931	The Bull by Thomas Allen
1931	Man and Child by Maurice Lambert
1931	Bust of Jacob Kramer by Loris Rey
c.1932	Bust of Donna Maria Chiapelli by Libero Andreotti
c.1932	Rose by Jacob Epstein
c.1932	Maquette for the Double Panel of Foliage for the Crown on the Figure of Charity on the Alexandria Memorial by Alfred Gilbert
1932	Bust of George V by William Reid Dick
1932	Cast of the Hands of Lord Berkeley Moynihan by Loris Rey
1932	Mother and Child by Henry Moore
c.1933	Europa by Edward Carter Preston
1933	Model of the Sculpture at Leeds Civic Hall: Putto with a Goat by Hermon Cawthra
1933	Model of the Sculpture at Leeds Civic Hall: Putto with a Turkey by Hermon Cawthra
1933	Lydia Laughing by Jacob Epstein
1933	Garden Roller: Adam and Eve by David Kindersley (after Eric Gill)
1933–5	The War God by Eric Kennington
c.1934	Bust of a Man by Donald Hastings
c.1935	Family by Leon Underwood
c.1935	Model of the Springbok at South Africa House, Trafalgar Square, London by Charles Wheeler
1935	Rotoreliefs by Marcel Duchamp
1935	Bending Figure by Frederick Edward McWilliam
c.1936	Bust of Margaret Rawlings, Lady Barlow by Frank Dobson
1936	Medal Commemorating the Launch of the Queen Mary by Gilbert Bayes
1936	Elsa by Jacob Epstein
1936	Marietta by Uli Nimptsch
1936	Medallion of Ellen Terry by Albert Toft
1936	Dish with a Little Boat by Paule Vezelay
1936	Mother and Child by Henry Moore
c.1937	Bank Holiday by Peter (Laszlo) Peri
1937	Maquette for a Knight on the Façade of County Hall, South Bank, London (x2) Alfred Hardiman
1937	Single Form by Barbara Hepworth
1937	The Dreamer by Laurence Josephs
1937	Forest by Paul Nash
1937	Only Egg by Paul Nash
1937	Fishing off the Pier by Peter (Laszlo)Peri
1937–9	Two in One by Gertrude Hermes
1938	Maquette for a Reclining Figure by Henry Moore
1938	General Gordon (plaster) by Harold J.Youngman
1939	Maquette for a Mobile by Alexander Calder
1939	Conicoid by Barbara Hepworth
1939	Bust of the Reverend Conrad Noel by Gertrude Hermes
1939	Stringed Figure by Henry Moore
1940s	Little People: a Woman of Authority by Peter (Laszlo) Peri
1940s	Little People: Woman with Folded Arms by Peter (Laszlo) Peri
1940	First Portrait of Ann Dobson by Frank Dobson
1941	Deirdre (First Portrait with Arms) by Jacob Epstein
1942	Bust of George Black by Jacob Epstein
1942	Emerging Form by Austin Wright
1944	Female Figure by Austin Wright
c.1945	Medallion to Karl Marx by Peter (Laszlo)Peri
c.1945	Medallion to the War of 1939–1945 by Peter (Laszlo)Peri
1945	Woman with Red Hair by Peter (Laszlo)Peri
1947	Maquette 'C' for the Sculpture at Waterloo Bridge, London by Barbara Hepworth
1948	Chicago Black by Alexander Calder
1948–9	Maquette for Linked Figures by Kenneth Armitage
c.1949	Female Figure by Emilio Greco
1949	Standing Figure by Kenneth Armitage
1949	Victor by Jacob Epstein
1949	Annunciation by Jocelyn Horner
1949	Forms on a Bow by Eduardo Paolozzi
1949 (cast 2002)	Playground (Game) by William Turnbull

c.1950	Maquette for a Wall Sculpture: Reclining Woman and Standing Child by Peter (Laszlo) Peri
c.1950	Maquette for a Public Sculpture: Boy and Girl Examining a Flask by Peter (Laszlo)Peri
1950	Maquette for The Word of God by Edward Bainbridge Copnall
1950	Mobile by Lynn Chadwick
1950	Bust of T. Edmund Harvey by Mark Harvey
1950	Medal for the Institute of Child Health, London by Gilbert Ledward
1951	Standing Group by Kenneth Armitage
1951	Maquette for the Lockheed Fountain 'Miranda' (x2) by Arthur Fleischmann
1951	Maquette for the Sunbathers by Peter (Laszlo) Peri
1951–4	Head by Geoffrey Clarke
c.1952	Maquette for Three Standing Figures by Kenneth Armitage
c.1952	Lamia by Francis William Sargant
1952	Maquette for Four Standing Figures by Kenneth Armitage
1952	Flat Standing Figure by Kenneth Armitage
1952	Maquette for Standing Group 2 (Version E) by Kenneth Armitage
1952	Maquette for Two Standing Figures by Kenneth Armitage
1952	The Paper Counters by Ghisha Koenig
1953	Two Standing Figures by Kenneth Armitage
1953	Children Playing by Kenneth Armitage
1953	Maquette for Footballers by Kenneth Armitage
1953	Tragic Group by Ralph Brown
1953	Hieroglyph by Barbara Hepworth
1954	Mother and Child by Ralph Brown
1954	Running Girl with Wheel by Ralph Brown
1954 (cast 1967)	Boy by Harry Phillips
1954	8 Maquettes for the Sculpture at the English Electric Company Headquarters on the Strand, London by Henry Moore
1954–5	Maquette for the Bronze Head of Karl Marx on the Marx Memorial in Highgate Cemetery, London by Laurence Bradshaw
mid-1950s	Maquette for a Monument: Woman and Child by Peter (Laszlo) Peri
1955	Roly Poly by Kenneth Armitage
1955	The Lesson by Franta Belsky
1955	Configuration (Phira) by Barbara Hepworth
1955	Untitled by Peter King

1955	Startled Bird by Bernard Meadows
1955	Maquette for Upright Motive No.3 by Henry Moore
1955	Maquette for the UNESCO Reclining Figure, Paris by Henry Moore
1955–7	Untitled by Peter King
1956	Girl by Reg Butler
1956	Smiling Head III (Smiling Woman) by Anthony Caro
1956	Crouching Man by Phillip King
1956	Hammerhead by Austin Wright
1956–7	Spatial Construction in Steel by Marlow Moss
1956–7	Girls in the Wind by Betty Rea
1957	Decorative Sculpture by Laurence Burt
1957	Standing Figure by John Warren Davis
1957	Abstract in Black, White, Cherry and Ochre by Victor Pasmore
1957–9	Maquette for The Neighbours by Siegfried Charoux
c.1958	The Gladiators by Leslie Thornton
1958	Icon by Hubert Dalwood
1958	AG5 by Eduardo Paolozzi
1958	Maquette for a Statue of a Miner at the Richborough Power Station, Kent by Harry Phillips
1958–9	Girl Without a Face by Kenneth Armitage
c.1959	Maquette for a Wall Relief at St. Michael's Primary School, Coventry: St. Michael Playing with Children by Peter (Laszlo) Peri
1959	Object–Open Square by Hubert Dalwood
1959	Blarney Sword by F.E. McWilliam
c.1960	Three by Fifteen by Winslow Foot
c.1960	Maquette for Dance by Alfred Horace Gerrard
1960	Threshold (Seuil Profil) by Jean Arp
1961	Maquette for a Relief Mural for the Sixth Congress of the International Union of Architects, South Bank, London by Anthony Hill
1961	Bust of a Rabbi by Lucy Lyons
1961	Resistance II by F. E. McWilliam
1962	Rising Movement 1 by Robert Adams
1962	Girl in a Window by Peter Blake
1962	Flag by Hubert Dalwood
1962	Unit Relief by Matt Rugg
1962	Moon by Austin Wright
c.1963	Head: Boat Form by Henry Moore
1963	Tower by Kenneth Armitage
1963	Standing Figure by John Hoskin
1963	Atom Body was Light by Liliane Lijn
1963	Blue Relief Painting by Frank Lisle

1963	Sign Elements III by Matt Rugg
1963	Three-Piece Reclining Figure No.2: Bridge Prop by Henry Moore
1964	Captive by George Fullard
1964	Old Money Bags by Bruce Lacey
1964	Untitled by E. R.Nele
1964	Poem for the Trio M.R.T. by Eduardo Paolozzi
1964	Wittgenstein at Cassino by Eduardo Paolozzi
1964	Red Circle by Harry Thubron
c.1965	Maquette by Neville Boden
c.1965	Wirefive by Winslow Foot
c.1965	Untitled by John Hoskin
c.1965	The Jungle by Bezalel Mann
1965	Wall by Kenneth Armitage
1965	Procession Through a Split Curve by Neville Boden
1965	The Titterary Tea Rose by Neville Boden
1965	Dual Form by Barbara Hepworth
1965	Through by Phillip King
1965	Hydroform by Roger Leigh
1965	Maquette for a Fountain at BP House, London by Mary Martin
1965	Chopper and Changer by Harry Seager
1965–6	Untitled (Pot) by Richard Long
1966	Bust of Sir Michael Tippett by Gertrude Hermes
1966	Diagonal Structure by Gunther Uecker
1967	Relief No.6 by Neville Boden
1967	Maquette for a Frieze at the Front of Leeds City Art Gallery by Hubert Dalwood
1967	Reflection by Peter Startup
1967	Relief Model of the Façade of Leeds City Art Gallery by Austin Wright
1967	Maquette for Section No.5 of a Frieze for the Façade of Leeds City Art Gallery by Austin Wright
1968	Two Lectures. Schemas 1 to 6 by Terry Atkinson
1968	Maquette for 3B Series, No.2 by Bernard Schottlander
1968	Series A No.II by William Tucker
1968	Maquette for a Three-Piece Sculpture: Vertebrae by Henry Moore
1969	Unword by Ian Breakwell and Mike Leggett
1969	Soft Drum Set by Claes Oldenburg
c.1970	Maquette for Column Landscape II by Hubert Dalwood
c.1970	Maquette for a Public Sculpture at the Euston Road Housing Estate, London by Bernard Schottlander
1970	Wedding Portrait by Martin Grose

1970	Calendar Shop I by Ghisha Koenig
1971	Ziggurat by Richard Oginz
1971	Maquette for Red Sandwich by Richard Oginz
1971	Postcard Work (x2) by David Tremlett
c.1972	Maquette for the Public Sculpture at the Office of National Statistics, Tredegar Park, Newport, Gwent by Hubert Dalwood
c.1972	Untitled/Horse by Keith Milow
1972	Single Figure with Drawing by Kenneth Armitage
1972	The Hands of Sir John Barbirolli by Jocelyn Horner
1972	But Drowning by Bruce James
1973	Location by Robert Morris
1973	A Young Girl Seated by her Window by Martin Naylor
1973	Paint Cupboard by Louise Parsons
c.1974	Maquette for Untitled by John Hoskin
1974	Helmet by Laurence Burt
1974	Maquettes for the Public Sculpture at the Haymarket Shopping Centre and Haymarket Theatre, Leicester (x2) by Hubert Dalwood
1974	Crossed Fingers by John Farnham
1975	Clay Figure by Barry Flanagan
1975	Time Remembered (Bronze) by Lucy Lyons
1975	Time Remembered (Wax) by Lucy Lyons
1975	Woman Undressing by Harry Phillips
c.1976	Woman with a Chair by Harry Phillips
1976	Menstrual Piece by Helen Chadwick
1976	Table I by Hubert Dalwood
1976	Maquette for Kangra II by Hubert Dalwood
1976	Maquette for South of the River by Bernard Schottlander
1976	Twenty Six Hours Vienna by Stuart Brisley
c.1977	Wordsworth Wadsworth by Ian Hamilton Finlay
1977	Screen by Julian Schwarz
1977–8	Emma Books by Anthony Caro
1978	Agony in the Garden by Anthony Earnshaw
1978	Important Mischief by Martin Naylor
1978	Three Heads No.21 by John Davies
1978	Arran Hilltops by Hamish Fulton
1978–9	National Grid by Anthony Caro
1979	Four Pietra Serena Wedges by Stephen Cox
1979	Crusoe's Dream by Anthony Earnshaw
1979	Raider's Bread by Anthony Earnshaw
1979	Wedge II by Garth Evans

c.1980	Pyramid by David Nash
1980	Colour Crucibles (Cluster II): Trefoil (x3) by Stephen Cox
1980	Colour Crucibles (Cluster II): Spiral by Stephen Cox
1980	Colour Crucibles (Cluster II): Bar (x2) by Stephen Cox
1980	Tondo: Disks I, II and III by Stephen Cox
1980	Broken Heart by John Farnham
1980	Tranquil Night by Michael Kenny
1980	Delabole Slate Circle by Richard Long
1980	Green Bronze IV by Michael Lyons
1980–1	Monument 1980–1: Colonial Version by Susan Hiller
1981	Majolica Dish by Stephen Cox
1981	Postcard Flag (Union Jack) by Tony Cragg
1981	Twin-Tub with Beaver by Bill Woodrow
1982	Fruit of Oblivion by Edward Allington
1982	The Cricketer by Barry Flanagan
1982	Seated Woman and Seated Man by Malcolm Woodward
1982	Girl on a Stool and Youth on a Chair by Malcolm Woodward
1982–3	Medicine Wheel by Chris Drury
1983	Untitled (Scarlet) by George Meyrick
1983	Medallion Commemorating the Henry Moore Exhibition 'Sculpture, Drawings and Graphics' at the Orangerie, Palais Auersperg, Vienna, Anonymous after Henry Moore
1984	Untitled (Terracotta) by George Meyrick
1984	Shelter by John Newling
1984	Tower by Charles Quick
1984	The Doppelganger by Stephen Willats
1985	Tanmatras by Stephen Cox
1985	Bronze Grid with Red by John Hoskin
1985	Glassworks by Ghisha Koenig
1985	Uomo by Harry Thubron
1986	Easy Chair by Stuart Brisley
c.1986–91	Maquettes for the Charing Cross Triple Starhead Commission, London: Starhead and Wake by Paul Neagu
1986	Maquette for the Leeds Brick Man by Antony Gormley
1986	Earth Above Ground by Antony Gormley
1986	Belgrano – Medal for Dishonour by Michael Sandle
1986	Maquette for XRL2 by Gillian Wise
1987	Red Fruit by Peter Randall-Page
1988	Held by Gerard Williams
1988	Small Stone Bridge by Glynn Williams
1988–89	32 Leafworks by Andy Goldsworthy
1989	Sugar by Edward Bainbridge
1989	Bowl XIII by Stephen Cox
1989	Penn Ponds in Winter by Andrew Sabin
1989–90	Garden Sculpture with Predetermined Details by Edward Allington
1990	Maquette for Nobody Here But Us (x3) by Richard Deacon
1990	Void Stone by Anish Kapoor
1990	Maquette for A Bottle of Notes (x2) by Claes Oldenburg
1991	Eat Me by Helen Chadwick
1991	(gold) Table by Grenville Davey
1991	I Fall to Pieces by Phill Hopkins
1991–2	Temper by Alison Wilding
1992	Six Dozen Red Roses by Anya Gallaccio
1992	Untitled 92-1 by Tessa Robins
1992	Untitled 92-5 by Tessa Robins
1993	Eight Bronzes by Edward Bainbridge
1993	Ten Commandments by Nicholas Pope
1993	Maquette for a Sculpture at the Christelijke Hogeschool, Leeuwarden by Auke de Vries
1994	Maquette for Almost Beautiful (x2) by Richard Deacon
1994	Couverture by Anya Gallaccio
1994	Black by Lucia Nogueira
1994	Gaia by Eric Peskett
1994	Maquette for a Large-Scale Sculpture by William Tucker
1995	Scape by Keith Wilson
1996	Extended Cube by David Nash
1997	Cold Face by Alison Wilding
1998	First Model for Eclipse by Langlands and Bell
1998	Second Model for Eclipse by Langlands and Bell
1999	Chalk Cliff Study by Boyle Family
2000	Return of Enos by Brian Griffiths
2001	In the Arms of Strangers by Jacqueline Donachie
2002	Bad Hat by Eva Rothschild

List of sculptors by date of birth

1585–1674	Caspar Gras
c.1604–1707	Jean Cavalier
fl.1630	Thomas Ventris
1630–1702	Filippo Parodi
1653–1741	Giuseppe Mazza
1667–1735	Jan Claudius de Cock
1677–1737	Andrew Carpenter
1691–1781	Peter Scheemakers
1695–1762	Louis Francois Roubiliac
1709–1787	John Cheere
1735–1805	Thomas Banks
1737–1823	Joseph Nollekens
1739–1799	Christopher Hewetson
1750–1820	Samuel Percy
1755–1826	John Flaxman
1757–1822	Antonio Canova
1770–1843	Berthel Thorvaldsen
1774–1839	Peter Turnerelli
1777–1818	George Bullock
1786–1860	Joseph Gott
1788–1856	Pierre Jean David d'Angers
1791–1850	Samuel Joseph
fl.1793–1850	David Morrison
1794–1864	William Behnes
fl.1794–1803	Alexis Decaix
1795–1850	Richard James Wyatt
1799–1878	Laurence MacDonald
1800–1883	Richard Cockle Lucas
1804–1891	William Theed
1805–1867	Carlo Marochetti
1807–1877	Henry Weekes
1809–1866	Edgar George Papworth
1809–1895	Mary Thornycroft
1810–1876	Thomas Earle
1811–1885	Edward William Wyon
1817–fl.1865	Alfred Bromley
1817–1897	William Day Keyworth
1818–1876	Matthew Noble
1818–1881	Raffaelle Monti
1819–1889	John Throp
1824–1887	Albert-Ernest Carrier-Belleuse
1825–1892	Thomas Woolner
1825–1895	Auguste van den Kerckhove
1828–1905	Henry Hugh Armstead
1830–1896	Frederick Leighton
1830–1910	John Adams Acton
1834–1890	Joseph Edward Boehm
1840–1917	Auguste Rodin
1846–1911	Louis-Oscar Roty
1846–1922	Isaac Cooke
1847–1910	John Macallan Swan
1847–1922	Thomas Brock
1848–1917	Edouard Lantéri
1848–1939	Princess Louise
1850–1925	William Hamo Thornycroft
1852–1901	Edward Onslow Ford
1854–1934	Alfred Gilbert
1855–1929	Michel Léonard Béguine
1855–1934	Ellen Mary Rope
1856–1909	Alexandre Louis Marie Charpentier
1857–1916	Thomas Stirling Lee
1858–1944	Alfred Drury
1860–1928	George Frampton
1860–?	Ella von Wrede
1862–1941	Ernest Sichel
1862–1949	Albert Toft
c.1866–1922	Edward Caldwell Spruce
1867–1940	Henry Charles Fehr
1868–1914	Mervyn Lawrence
1870–1960	Francis William Sargant
1871–1926	Francis Derwent Wood
1872–1953	Gilbert Bayes
1875–1933	Libero Andreotti
1876–1938	Robert Tait McKenzie
1877–?	Kuhne Beveridge
1878–1947	Kathleen Scott
1879–1961	William Reid Dick
1880–1939	Frances Darlington
1880–1955	Anders Olsen
1880–1959	Jacob Epstein

1880–1977	Naum Gabo	1907–1969	Mary Martin
1882–1940	Eric Gill	1908–1998	Victor Pasmore
1883–1959	David Evans	1909–1992	F.E. McWilliam
1883–1962	Ivan Meštrović	1911–1976	Harry Phillips
1885–1965	Edward Carter Preston	1911–1997	Austin Wright
1885–1934	Charles Sargeant Jagger	b.1913	Mark Harvey
1885–1966	Jean Arp	1913–1981	Reg Butler
1886–1963	Frank Dobson	1913–1995	Emilio Greco
1886–1972	Hermon Cawthra	1913–1998	Laurence Josephs
1887–1968	Marcel Duchamp	1914–2003	Lynn Chadwick
1887–c.1973	Harold J. Youngman	c.1915–fl.1987	Thomas Allen
1888–c.1939	Frederick John Wilcoxson	b.1915	Bernard Meadows
1888–1960	Eric Kennington	1915–1985	Harry Thubron
1888–1960	Gilbert Ledward	1915–1995	David Kindersley
1889–1946	Paul Nash	b.1916	Frank Lisle
c.1890–1953	Barry Hart	1916–2002	Kenneth Armitage
1890–1958	Marlow Moss	1916–2003	Lucy Lyons
1890–1975	Leon Underwood	b.1917	Bezalel Mann
1891–1915	Henri Gaudier-Brzeska	1917–1984	Robert Adams
1891–1949	Alfred Hardiman	1917–1997	Eric Peskett
1892–1974	Charles Wheeler	b.1919	John Warren Davis
1892–1984	Paule Vézelay	1921–1976	Peter Startup
1896–1967	Siegfried Charoux	1921–1990	John Hoskin
1896–1990	Arthur Fleischmann	1921–1993	Ghisha Koenig
1897–1977	Uli Nimptsch	1921–2000	Franta Belsky
1898–1976	Alexander Calder	b.1922	William Turnbull
1898–1986	Henry Moore	1923–1973	George Fullard
1899–1978	Laurence Bradshaw	b.1924	Phyllis M. Blundell
1899–1967	Peter (Laszlo) Peri	b.1924	Anthony Caro
1899–1998	Alfred Horace Gerrard	b.1924	Geoffrey Clarke
1900–1938	Donald Hastings	1924–1976	Hubert Dalwood
1901–1964	Maurice Lambert	1924–1999	Bernard Schottlander
1901–1983	Gertrude Hermes	1924–2001	Anthony Earnshaw
1902–1967	Harold James Dow	1924–2005	Eduardo Paolozzi
1902–1973	Jocelyn Horner	b.1925	Laurence Burt
1903–1962	Loris Rey	b.1925	Ian Hamilton Finlay
1903–1973	Edward Bainbridge Copnall	b.1925	Roger Leigh
1903–1975	Barbara Hepworth	b.1925	Leslie Thornton
1904–1965	Betty Rea	b.1927	Bruce Lacey
1906–1985	Oscar Nemon	1927–2002	John Bunting

b.1928	Ralph Brown		b.1945	David Nash
1928–1957	Peter King		b.1945	David Tremlett
1929–1996	Neville Boden		b.1946	Stephen Cox
b.1929	Claes Oldenburg		b.1946	John Davies
b.1930	Anthony Hill		b.1946	Hamish Fulton
b.1930	Gunther Uecker		b.1948	Chris Drury
b.1931	Robert Morris		b.1948	Alison Wilding
b.1931	Harry Seager		b.1948	Bill Woodrow
b.1932	Peter Blake		b.1949	Tony Cragg
b.1932	E. R. Nele		b.1949	Richard Deacon
b.1933	Stuart Brisley		b.1949	Nicholas Pope
b.1933	Martin Grose		b.1949	Julian Schwarz
b.1934	Garth Evans		1950–1998	Lucia Nogueira
b.1934	Phillip King		b.1950	Antony Gormley
b.1935	Matt Rugg		b.1951	Edward Allington
b.1935	William Tucker		b.1952	John Newling
b.1936	Michael Sandle		1953–1996	Helen Chadwick
b.1936	Gillian Wise		b.1953	George Meyrick
b.1937	Auke de Vries		b.1954	Anish Kapoor
1938–2004	Paul Neagu		b.1954	Peter Randall-Page
b.1939	Terry Atkinson		b.1955	Eric Bainbridge
b.1939	Winslow Foot		b.1955	Ben Langlands
b.1939	Bruce James		b.1956	Andy Goldsworthy
b.1939	Liliane Lijn		b.1957	Charles Quick
b.1939	Glynn Williams		b.1958	Andrew Sabin
b.1940	Susan Hiller		b.1959	Nikki Bell
b.1941	Barry Flanagan		b.1959	Gerard Williams
1941–1999	Michael Kenny		b.1961	Grenville Davey
b.1942	John Farnham		b.1961	Phill Hopkins
1943–2004	Carl Plackman		b.1963	Anya Gallaccio
1943–2005	Ian Breakwell		b.1965	Tessa Robins
b.1943	Mike Lyons		b.1965	Keith Wilson
b.1943	Stephen Willats		b.1968	Brian Griffiths
b.1943	Malcolm Woodward		b.1969	Jacqueline Donachie
b.1944	Martin Naylor		b.1972	Eva Rothschild
b.1944	Richard Oginz			
b.1944	Louise Parsons			
b.1945	Michael Leggett			
b.1945	Richard Long			
b.1945	Keith Milow			

Index of sitters